Contents

Acknowledgements

Authors

Dr ES Williams	Epidemiological Advisor, West Sussex PCT
Anna Kirk	Public Health Programme Manager, West Sussex PCT
Clare Harmer	Public Health Observatory Manager, West Sussex PCT

Contributors

Dr Farhang Tahzib	Joint Director of Public Health and Well-being, West Sussex PCT and West Sussex County Council
Catherine Scott	Consultant in Public Health, West Sussex PCT
David Smith	Area Director: Sussex and Surrey, Learning Skills Council South East
Aidan Pettitt	Partnership Director, Learning Skills Council Sussex
Jacqueline Clay	Shared Intelligence Manager, West Sussex County Council
Jane Williams	Public Health Specialist in Substance Misuse, West Sussex PCT and West Sussex Drug and Alcohol Action Team
Dr Gemma Ward	Public Health Doctor, West Sussex PCT
Lesley Wilkes	Public Health Information Analyst, West Sussex PCT
Versha Talati	Senior Public Health Nutrition/Obesity Lead, West Sussex PCT
Graeme Potter	Health Improvement Specialist Practitioner: Mental Health, West Sussex PCT
Nicola Coleridge	Health Improvement Specialist Practitioner: Physical Activity, West Sussex PCT
Paul Woodcock	Public Health Programme Manager: Sexual Health, West Sussex PCT
Christine Beveridge	Tobacco Control Co-ordinator, West Sussex PCT

Foreword

This excellent piece of work provides West Sussex with an important and timely insight into the health and educational determinants of young adults in further and higher education. Up until now there has been little accurate information on the lifestyles and attitudes of young people in the 16 – 24 years age group. The needs of young adults, at this crucial time of transition must be given the attention they deserve.

This far-reaching survey is a result of collaboration between the West Sussex Public Health Observatory, the Learning Skills Council and the major further and higher education establishments of West Sussex. It investigates the views and fundamental issues affecting the young people of West Sussex today.

This report provides a voice for this often overlooked section of the community. The information gathered will prove invaluable in advancing the understanding of this age group, ensuring the gap between child and adult services is bridged and easing the challenges faced by teenagers in their transition to adulthood. It is essential intelligence for policy makers, commissioners and local communities to address the issues raised.

All information presented here has been provided by young people themselves; their enthusiastic support, along with that of their college tutors, is gratefully acknowledged.

We believe this report provides a solid foundation for effective joint working between health, further and higher education and the Learning Skills Council to ensure that the West Sussex Sustainable Community Strategy and the 'Local Area Agreement' for West Sussex take full account of the needs and aspirations of this vital age range of young people.

Dr Farhang Tahzib
Joint Director of Public Health and Well-being,
West Sussex PCT and West Sussex County Council

David Smith
Area Director: Sussex and Surrey, LSC South East

Introduction

There are very few surveys that focus on young adults. The reason why lifestyle behaviours of young adults are less well researched than other age groups is because they are difficult to reach. They are no longer in school and they tend to have poor response rates to postal surveys. Yet early adult life is a time when behaviour, thinking and beliefs are undergoing rapid change. It is important that services understand the needs of this group so that appropriate policies and services can be developed.

Background

This lifestyle survey of 16 to 24-year-olds attending Further and Higher Education Colleges in West Sussex was conducted in the winter term 2006-2007. It was carried out by West Sussex Public Health Observatory in partnership with the Learning Skills Council and Colleges of Further and Higher Education in West Sussex.

Aims of the survey

1. To describe the health and social behaviour of young adults attending Further and Higher Education colleges in West Sussex.

2. To estimate the prevalence of risk behaviour among young adults, such as cigarette smoking, the use of illicit drugs and alcohol consumption.

3. To gather data on the sexual behaviour of young adults.

4. To make the findings of the survey available to colleges, local residents and to the statutory agencies with responsibility for addressing the health and social needs of young adults.

5. To provide information to assist the planning of health promotion initiatives aimed at young adults.

Sample frame for the study

The aim was to collect data from a sample of young adults that was large enough to allow the analysis of sub groups. The questionnaires were distributed to students aged 16 to 24-years-old who were attending the three main FE and HE colleges in West Sussex: Northbrook College, Chichester College and Central Sussex College.

It should be remembered that the FE and HE college population consists of students who are undertaking education or training in specific work related areas defined on the college websites as 'cultural and creative industries'. When interpreting the results it should be borne in mind that the sample is highly selected, that those who chose to respond may have particular characteristics and that this group is not necessarily representative of all young adults in this age group living in the county. Young adults not attending FE colleges were excluded from the survey because there was no systematic way to identify and engage with them that would result in robust quantitative data.

Despite these limitations, the data does give a useful snap shot of the lives of a large proportion of young adults in the county.

Limitations of cross-sectional surveys

The purpose of a cross-sectional survey is to provide descriptive epidemiology of a specified population by describing the prevalence of certain behaviours, risk factors and the relationships between them. For example, it may describe the frequency of cigarette smoking as well as showing the relationship between those who smoke and those who drink alcohol.

Cross-sectional studies provide information from which useful inferences can be made and from which hypotheses can be generated. However, it is seldom possible to establish causal relationships from cross-sectional data.

Tests of significance

As there is no hypothesis being tested in this report, the decision was made not to include tests of significance as to do so may be misleading. This report describes relationships between various risk factors and to report significant differences might go beyond what the data allows. Moreover, because of the large numbers in the survey most cross tabulations produce a significant chi squared statistical test (p value). However even though it can be stated that, for example, there is a definite relationship between smoking and family structure, it cannot be concluded which particular family group is significantly different from any other.

Questionnaire Design

A local questionnaire was designed for the survey using validated questions from other surveys where appropriate. Stakeholders including health and education professionals and policy makers around the county were consulted during the development stage. The philosophy behind the questionnaire was to get an overview on a wide range of issues rather than looking at selected topics in depth. A number of focus groups were held with students from the various colleges in order to ensure issues important to their health were included.

The questionnaire was piloted with a number of students and appropriate changes were made.

Data Collection

Arrangements were made with each college to distribute questionnaires to the student body. There was a covering letter stressing that respondents would remain anonymous. Completed questionnaires were returned to the West Sussex Public Health Observatory.

Consent

All respondents were aged 16 or over and were given information on the survey prior to completion. Any students who did not wish to participate were given the opportunity to withdraw.

Response rate

In view of the logistical problems in contacting the student body it was not possible to estimate the exact number of questionnaires received by students and calculate a precise denominator, as some do not attend college regularly but are on placements.

The aim was to collect as many questionnaires as possible from each college, taking the pragmatic view that the larger the number of complete questionnaires, the more likely the data was to be reasonably representative of the student body. The total number of questionnaires completed was 2,672. We estimate that 20% of registered students completed a questionnaire.

Data Entry

Information from the questionnaire was scanned and entered into a database. Data was checked for errors and then cleaned for analysis using Microsoft Access and Statistical Package for Social Sciences (SPSS). The West Sussex Public Health Observatory undertook the data analysis.

Missing data and rounding

In line with other surveys of this nature not every respondent answered every question. The data is presented showing those who responded to the questions and it is noted wherever the proportion of missing responses is high. Due to rounding not all percentages sum to 100 per cent. All percentages are presented to one decimal place.

Geographical analysis based upon postcode

In total 60.8% of students reported their postcode on the questionnaire (see Table 1.1). Numbers for some of the local authority areas are too small to draw any conclusions for individual questions; consequently results by local authority are not shown in this report.

Table 1.2 compares the proportions of respondents from each local authority with those registered with a GP, and broadly the respondents are proportionately similar. It should be acknowledged that this includes only those who gave their postcodes.

Table 1.1 Proportion of respondents by postcode

Local authority	N	(%)
Adur	74	(2.8)
Arun	249	(9.3)
Chichester	197	(7.4)
Crawley	180	(6.7)
Horsham	140	(5.2)
Mid Sussex	359	(13.4)
Worthing	241	(9.0)
Out of county	185	(7.0)
No postcode	1047	(39.2)

Table 1.2 Proportions in each Local Authority area (who gave their postcode) compared with Exeter GP registration data (March 2007)

Local authority	Survey 16-24-year-olds (%)	Exeter data (16-24-year-olds) (%)
Adur	5	8
Arun	17	18
Chichester	14	14
Crawley	13	15
Horsham	10	15
Mid Sussex	25	17
Worthing	17	13
Total	100	100

The characteristics of the survey population

This section of the report describes the demographic profile of the survey population of young adults attending Further Education (FE) and Higher Education (HE) colleges in West Sussex. The number of completed questionnaires received for analysis was 2,672, with the largest number coming from Chichester College (1,149), followed by Central Sussex College (823) and Northbrook College (698).

Age sex breakdown

More male students (58.3%) than female students (41.7%) responded. The majority of the sample were aged 16, 17 or 18, and 20.9% were aged 20 years or over. Table 2.1 shows the age sex breakdown of the survey population.

Ethnicity

Students were asked to indicate their ethnic group from categories similar to those listed in the 2001 Census. The majority of students (91.9%) were White with 2.7% Asian (Indian = 0.5%, Pakistani = 0.7%, Other Asian =1.4%), 1.7% Mixed, 1.2% Black, 1.1% Chinese and 1.2% belonging to other ethnic groups. Because of the small numbers in most ethnic groups it was not possible to undertake much analysis by this variable.

Religion

Two questions were asked about religion. Religious affiliation indicates the religion with which a student associates, and religious observance is a measure of how frequently a student attends a meeting or service. Table 2.2 shows religious affiliation.

Just over half of the survey population has no religious affiliation. Church of England is the most common religion (28.1%), followed by Other Christian (8.1%) and Roman Catholicism (5.7%). A small proportion of students were affiliated to Islam (1.6%), Buddhism (1.1%), Hinduism (0.8%), Sikhism (0.4%) and Judaism (0.3%). Because the numbers for some religions are small, the survey data has been analysed by the four largest groups: the three branches of the Christian religion and no religion.

Table 2.1 Age sex breakdown

Age group	Males		Females		All	
	N	(%)	N	(%)	N	(%)
16	244	(16.0)	191	(17.4)	435	(16.6)
17	584	(38.2)	494	(44.9)	1078	(41.0)
18	350	(22.9)	217	(19.7)	567	(21.6)
19	146	(9.6)	97	(8.8)	243	(9.2)
20 and over	204	(13.4)	101	(9.2)	305	(11.6)
All ages	1,528	(100.0)	1,100	(100.0)	2628	(100.0)

Table 2.2 Religious affiliation by sex

	Males		Females		All	
	N	(%)	N	(%)	N	(%)
Church of England	390	(26.3)	328	(30.6)	718	(28.1)
Other Christian	100	(6.7)	107	(10.0)	207	(8.1)
Roman Catholic	74	(5.0)	71	(6.6)	145	(5.7)
No religion	781	(52.6)	512	(47.8)	1,293	(50.6)
Other	140	(9.4)	53	(4.9)	193	(7.6)
All	1,485	(100.0)	1,071	(100.0)	2,556	(100.0)

There are large differences when looking at religious observance, as shown in Figure 2.1. Of those affiliated to the Church of England 89.8% attend a religious service about once a year and 5.9% attend weekly. Three quarters of Roman Catholics attend yearly and around 12.5% weekly. Highest attendance is by those affiliated to Other Christian churches with 26.8% attending weekly. The majority of students with no religious affiliation (97.4%) attend a religious meeting yearly or less.

Figure 2.1 Religious affiliation by religious observance

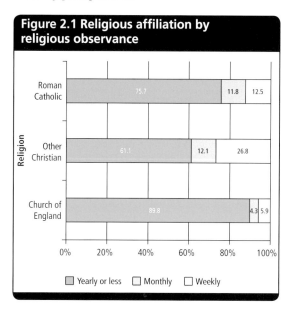

■ Yearly or less □ Monthly □ Weekly

Marital status

To take account of recent changes in legislation the question on marital status included the option of civil partnership. The vast majority of responding students are single (93.4%), with only a small proportion married (1.0%) and a few who are divorced, separated or widowed (1.0%). A small number of students reported being in a civil partnership (4.6%). Civil partnership, a relatively new concept, may have caused confusion as a number of students who reported being in a civil partnership also reported themselves as heterosexual.

Living arrangements

A large proportion of students (87%) are living with their parents, 2.8% live on their own, 2.8% with partners and 2.2% live in university accommodation. The other 5% live with friends or have other* living arrangements.

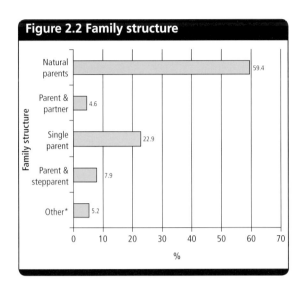

Figure 2.2 Family structure

(Family structure, %)

- Natural parents: 59.4
- Parent & partner: 4.6
- Single parent: 22.9
- Parent & stepparent: 7.9
- Other*: 5.2

Family structure of students living with parents

To ascertain the family structure, the 87% of students who were living with their parents were asked with whom they mainly lived. Just over 59.4% live with their mother and father, 4.6% with mother/father and partner, 7.9% with a stepparent, 22.9% with a single parent. Just over 5% reside in an other* family arrangement, which, for this report, includes living with relatives/guardian, in a care home, or in foster care.

Employment

Table 2.3 shows the employment status of students. Just less than three-quarters of students (72.5%) are in some form of employment. Male students are more likely to be in full time employment (20.0%) than female students (3.5%).

Table 2.3 Employment status by sex

	Males		Females	
	N	(%)	N	(%)
Full time	294	(20.0)	38	(3.5)
Part time	751	(50.3)	742	(68.8)
Not employed	428	(29.1)	298	(27.6)
Total	1,473	(100.0)	1,078	(100.0)

There is a strong age gradient: the older the student, the more likely they are to be in employment. Students who are 19 or over are more likely to be working full time (24.8%) than those aged under 19 (9.8%). Part time work is more common among the under 19s than those aged 19 or over (61.2%, 48.9% respectively).

Figure 2.3 shows the main source of money by age. As expected, the trend for parental contribution decreases with age and the proportion of money from employment increases.

Students who are 19 years of age or over are more likely to often worry about money (37.7%) than those aged 16, 17 or 18-years-old (23.4%, 25.8% and 32.2% respectively).

Children

Around five per cent of students (4.7%) reported that they had children, with 70.0% of them classifying themselves as not married.

General health

Students were asked to make a self-assessment of their health over the last 12 months. The response is shown in Table 2.4. While 6.6% of the student population perceive their general health as not good, females are more likely to report poorer health than males.

Table 2.4 General health by sex

	Males	Females	All
	(%)		
Good	59.8	48.9	55.2
Fairly good	34.1	44.0	38.2
Not good	6.2	7.1	6.6
Total	100.0	100.0	100.0

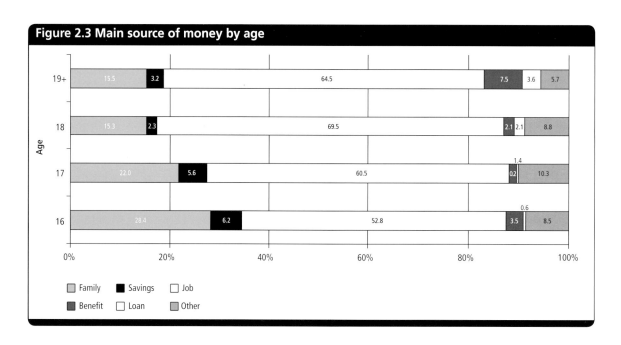

Figure 2.3 Main source of money by age

Age	Family	Savings	Job	Benefit	Loan	Other
19+	15.5	3.2	64.5	7.5	3.6	5.7
18	15.3	2.3	69.5	2.1	2.1	8.8
17	22.0	5.6	60.5	1.4	0.2	10.3
16	28.4	6.2	52.8	0.6	3.5	8.5

Legend: Family, Savings, Job, Benefit, Loan, Other

Comments

1. The aim of this report is to analyse lifestyle issues by a range of important social variables.

2. The small number of students in some ethnic groups means that it is not possible to analyse data by this variable.

3. Similarly, there are small numbers for some religious affiliations. As it is not appropriate to group together religions with different beliefs, the main branches of the Christian faith and those with no religion have been used for further analysis.

4. As most students live at home with their parents, it is possible to analyse lifestyle factors by family structure.

* Other family arrangement includes living with relatives/guardian, in a care home, in foster care.

Smoking

Cigarette smoking remains a major threat to public health. There is ample evidence to show the serious effects of smoking on general health and well-being. While there is some evidence to suggest that the ban on smoking in public places has had an impact on smoking levels in general, it is not yet clear to what degree it has affected smoking levels among young people.

Smoking peaked in the 1950s and 1960s then fell steadily in the 1970s and 1980s. The long downward trend in smoking appears to be levelling out. Since the early 1990s in Great Britain the prevalence of cigarette smoking has been highest in the 20 to 24- year-old age group.

The Health Survey for England shows that among young adults (16-24-year-olds) the proportions reporting current cigarette smoking decreased from 36% to 28% among males and from 38% to 29% among females between 1997 and 2006[1]. In the 2006 survey, 67% of young men and 66% of young women said they had never regularly smoked cigarettes, and 5% of young men and 6% of young women were ex-regular smokers.

The Smoking Kills target for smoking among adults is to reduce rates of adult smoking by 26% by 2005 and 21% by 2010[2]. The most recent data suggests both men and women have met the 2005 milestone, with overall smoking prevalence falling to 24% in 2005. The 2010 target is likely to be achieved.

Smoking prevalence

Students were asked to describe their smoking status. Table 3.1 shows a different pattern of smoking between males and females, with more young men (29.6%) than young women (24.4%) reporting that they are regular smokers. A further 13.0% of males and 15.0% of females were occasional smokers. As can be seen from Table 3.1, the proportion of current smokers (occasional and regular together) among males is 42.6% and among females is 39.4%.

Table 3.1 Smoking by sex						
Smoking status	Males		Females		All	
	N	(%)	N	(%)	N	(%)
Never smoked	709	(46.5)	540	(49.5)	1249	(47.7)
Given up	166	(10.9)	121	(11.1)	287	(11.0)
Occasional	198	(13.0)	164	(15.0)	362	(13.8)
Regular	452	(29.6)	266	(24.4)	718	(27.4)
Total	1525	(100.0)	1091	(100.0)	2616	(100.0)

Table 3.2 Occasional and regular smoking by age (%)

Age	Males		Females	
	Occasional	Regular	Occasional	Regular
16	12.0	27.4	14.0	26.3
17	13.9	29.3	16.2	22.8
18	11.7	31.1	15.8	29.3
19	13.4	26.8	14.4	18.6
20+	13.9	31.2	11.1	24.2

Smoking by age group

The prevalence of occasional and regular smoking by age is shown in Table 3.2. Among males there is little difference across the age range, with over 40% of males being current smokers (occasional and regular together) in all ages except for 16-year-olds (39.4%). Among females smoking rates tend to be higher among the younger ages. For example, 40.3% of 16-year-olds are current smokers compared with 33.0% of 19-year-olds. Highest rates of current smoking are in males aged over 20 and females aged 18 (45.1% in both groups).

Figure 3.1 shows the number of cigarettes smoked per day. Even though more females (23.1%) than males (18.1%) smoke less than one cigarette per day, the median number of cigarettes smoked per day is 10 for both sexes and the overall pattern of smoking is similar. The mean number of cigarettes smoked per day by males was 11.5 and females 10.5.

Regular smoking by religion and family structure

Figure 3.2 shows regular smoking by religious affiliation. Highest rates of regular smoking are in those with no religion, followed by Roman Catholics and Church of England. Among students affiliated to Islam 15.0% were regular smokers, while among Sikhs 66.7% were regular smokers, although the small numbers in these groups should be acknowledged.

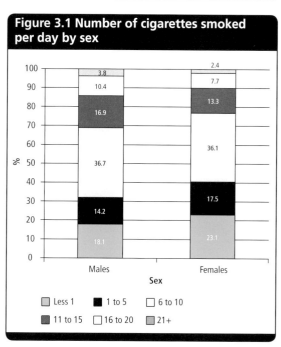

Figure 3.1 Number of cigarettes smoked per day by sex

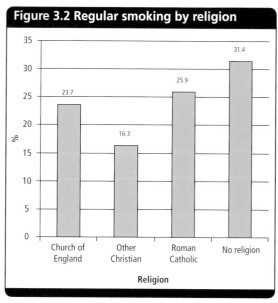

Figure 3.2 Regular smoking by religion

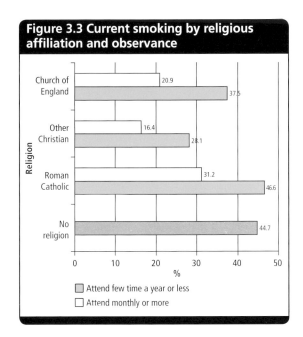

Figure 3.3 Current smoking by religious affiliation and observance

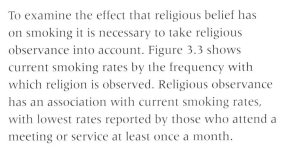

Figure 3.4 Regular smoking by family structure

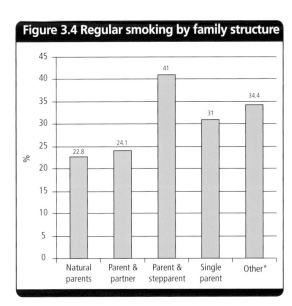

To examine the effect that religious belief has on smoking it is necessary to take religious observance into account. Figure 3.3 shows current smoking rates by the frequency with which religion is observed. Religious observance has an association with current smoking rates, with lowest rates reported by those who attend a meeting or service at least once a month.

Family Structure

Regular smoking is highest among students who live in stepparent families (41.0%), other* family arrangements (34.4%) and single parent families (31.0%).

Smoking and health

Regular smokers are three times more likely to regard their health as not good (12.5%) than those who have never smoked (3.7%).

Figure 3.5 Health status not good by smoking status

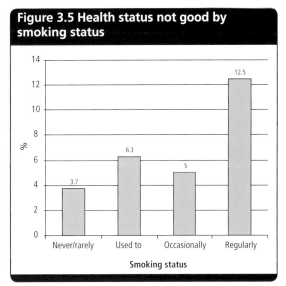

Comments

1. The rate of regular and current smoking is surprisingly high among young people attending West Sussex Colleges of Further and Higher Education. The rate of current smokers in this survey was higher than the rates reported in The Health Survey for England 2006: in this survey the rate of current smokers among males was 42.6% and females 39.4%, compared with 28% for young men and 29% for young women reported in the Health Survey of England.[3]

2. A survey of West Sussex schoolchildren reported that 9% of boys and 15% of girls aged 15 were regular smokers. In this survey 27% of male students and 26% of female students aged 16 were regular smokers. This suggests either a dramatic increase in smoking as young people enter college life, or that smoking rates are higher among young people who go on to Further and Higher Education .

3. Religious observance and family structure are associated with levels of smoking.

4. Self-perceived health status data shows that regular smokers are over three times more likely to perceive their health status as not good.

* Other family arrangement includes living with relatives/guardian, in a care home, or in foster care.

[1] The Health Survey for England 2006. The Department of Health 2007

[2] Smoking Kills: A White Paper on tobacco. Department of Health 1999

[3] The Health Survey for England 2006. The Department of Health 2007

Alcohol

Frequent news headlines suggest that young adults in the UK have a growing problem with alcohol. The Office for National Statistics has reported that the number of alcohol related deaths has more than doubled over the last decade.

The Government's alcohol strategy (Alcohol Harm Reduction Strategy 2004), published in March 2004, aims to prevent a further increase in alcohol related harms in England[1]. The updated strategy aims to minimise the health harms, violence and anti-social behaviour associated with alcohol, whilst ensuring that people are able to enjoy alcohol safely and responsibly. It specifically focuses on the minority of drinkers who cause the most harm to themselves, their communities and their families. The strategy's objectives also include educating young adults so they can make informed choices about alcohol and restricting the supply of alcohol to underage drinkers.

Experience with alcohol

Table 4.1 shows that 35.7% of males reported that they regularly consume alcohol compared with 22.7% of females. Around one in six students (17.4%) never or rarely consume alcohol.

The lowest rates of regular alcohol consumption are reported by Black (17.9%) and Asian students (21.7%). There is an age effect with students aged 16 and 17 having lower levels of regular drinking (24.0% and 28.0% respectively) than those aged 19 and over (33.0%).

Religion and family structure

Religious affiliation is associated with regular alcohol consumption: Other Christians (17.2%) and Roman Catholics (24.8%) have the lowest rates of consumption. The frequency of regular alcohol consumption among students affiliated to Islam was 7.9%, Hinduism 15.0% and Buddhism 50.0% (although small sample sizes need to be acknowledged).

Table 4.1 Experience with alcohol by sex	Males		Females		All	
	N	(%)	N	(%)	N	(%)
Never/rarely	261	(17.1)	197	(17.9)	458	(17.4)
Occasionally	720	(47.2)	653	(59.4)	1373	(52.3)
Regularly	545	(35.7)	249	(22.7)	794	(30.2)
Total	1,526	(100.0)	1,099	(100.0)	2,625	(100.0)

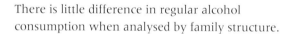

Figure 4.1 Regular alcohol consumption by religious affiliation

There is little difference in regular alcohol consumption when analysed by family structure.

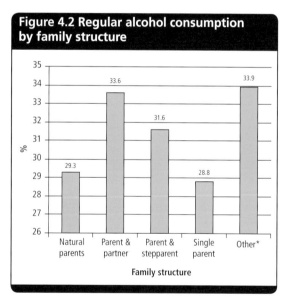

Figure 4.2 Regular alcohol consumption by family structure

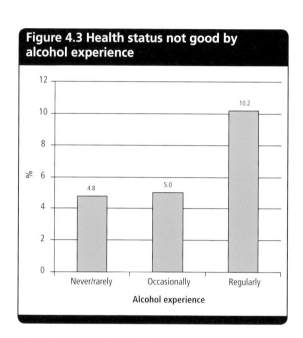

Figure 4.3 Health status not good by alcohol experience

Alcohol and health

Students who regularly consume alcohol are twice as likely as those who never or rarely drink alcohol to regard their health as not good.

Binge drinking

A quarter of the students admitted to binge drinking regularly and a further 47.8% do so occasionally. Young men are more likely to regularly binge drink (29.8%) than young women (18.8%).

Binge drinking is defined as 'drinking with the intention of getting drunk'.

Table 4.2 Binge drinking by sex						
Binge drinking	Males		Females		All	
	N	(%)	N	(%)	N	(%)
Never/rarely	364	(25.2)	303	(29.5)	667	(27.0)
Occasionally	649	(44.9)	531	(51.7)	1,180	(47.8)
Regularly	431	(29.8)	193	(18.8)	624	(25.3)
Total	1,444	(100.0)	1,027	(100.0)	2,471	(100.0)

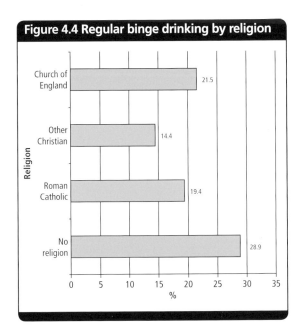

Figure 4.4 Regular binge drinking by religion

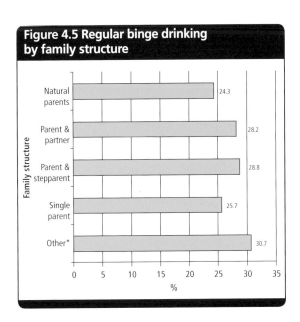

Figure 4.5 Regular binge drinking by family structure

While there are large differences in binge drinking by religion, there are none by family structure (Figure 4.5). As shown in Figure 4.4, students with no religion (28.9%) were twice as likely as Other Christians (14.4%) to regularly binge drink.

Alcohol and smoking

There is a relationship between smoking and drinking alcohol, as shown in Figure 4.6. More than half (52.5%) of males who are regular smokers also regularly drink alcohol, compared with only 20.5% of those who have never smoked. A similar pattern is present among females, although at lower levels.

Health status by smoking and alcohol use

Regular smoking is more strongly associated with poor self-perceived health status than regular drinking. Among those who regularly drink but have never smoked, 5.5% perceive their health status as not good compared with 12.2% of those who rarely or never drink but who regularly smoke. Almost one in seven (15.8%) of students who regularly smoke and drink report that their health is not good.

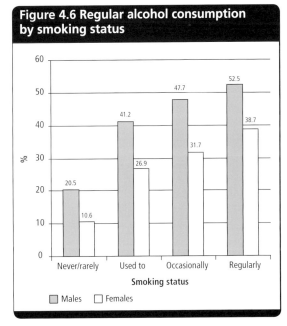

Figure 4.6 Regular alcohol consumption by smoking status

Table 4.3 Health status by smoking and alcohol use

Smoking experience	Alcohol consumption	Health status (%) not good
Never/rarely	Never/rarely	4.3
Never/rarely	Regularly	5.5
Regularly	Never/rarely	12.2
Regularly	Regularly	15.8

Comments

1. One in three males and one in four females reported that they regularly consume alcohol.

2. A quarter of young adults admit to regularly binge drinking (29.8% of males and 18.8% of females.)

3. International evidence suggests that identifying alcohol misuse early and offering simple advice can help to reduce alcohol consumption to more sensible levels.

4. The growing epidemic of alcohol problems in the UK is associated with road accidents, violence, public disorder, illness and premature death.

* Other family arrangement includes living with relatives/guardian, in a care home, or in foster care.

[1] Alcohol Harm Reduction Strategy, Prime Minster's Strategy Unit, Cabinet Office, March 2004.

Drugs

Drug misuse can have serious implications on the health and well-being of individual users as well as on their families, friends and communities. Tackling drug misuse is high on the Government's agenda with an annual spend of £1.5billion[1]. A central aim of the Government's drug strategy is to prevent today's young people becoming tomorrow's problem drug users[2].

Public Service Agreement Target:

'to reduce the use of Class A drugs and the frequent use of any illicit drug by all young people under the age of 25, especially by the most vulnerable groups'.

The Home Office

Due to the concern about the mental health effects and the availability of stronger forms of the drug, in July 2007, the Government commissioned a review to consider whether to re-classify cannabis as a class B drug. The review recommended that cannabis remain a class C drug, but described it as a "significant public health issue". However, in May 2008, the Government announced (subject to Parliamentary approval) that cannabis was to be reclassified back to a class B drug.

Cannabis

For the purpose of this report a current cannabis user is defined as someone who reported regularly or occasionally using the drug.

In line with the national trend the most commonly used drug by students is cannabis. Half of males and a third of females have used cannabis at least once. The difference between the sexes is particularly noticeable among the regular users of cannabis with 10.9% of males stating they are regular users compared with 2.5% of females (Table 5.1).

As expected, experience of cannabis increases with age although it is the 18-year-old age group that has the highest proportion of current users (26.0%) (See Figure 5.1).

Table 5.1 Cannabis experience by sex

	Males		Females		All	
	N	(%)	N	(%)	N	(%)
Never/rarely	756	(50.8)	706	(66.7)	1,462	(57.4)
Used to	311	(20.9)	183	(17.3)	494	(19.4)
Occasionally	259	(17.4)	144	(13.6)	403	(15.8)
Regularly	163	(10.9)	26	(2.5)	189	(7.4)
Total	1,489	(100.0)	1,059	(100.0)	2,548	(100.0)

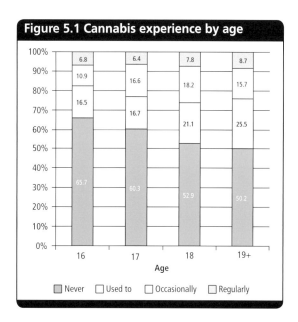

Figure 5.1 Cannabis experience by age

As can be seen in Figure 5.2, current cannabis use varies by family structure with the highest proportion of users (30.6%) living in other* family arrangements.

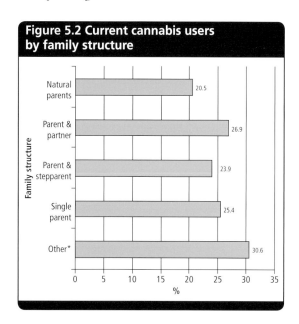

Figure 5.2 Current cannabis users by family structure

Of those students with no religion, 27.1% are current cannabis users. The lowest proportion of current cannabis users is seen amongst those who identify with the Church of England (16.3%) and Other Christian (16.9%) religion.

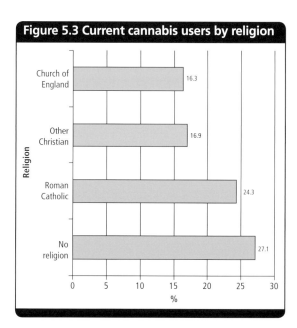

Figure 5.3 Current cannabis users by religion

Other drug use

For use of drugs other than cannabis respondents were not given the option to state *'used to but have now stopped'* or *'tried once'*. As students' reported drug use is self-perceived, it is not clear whether respondents classified experimental drug use as occasional or never used.

As shown in Table 5.2, the survey asked whether students had never, occasionally or regularly taken a number of other drugs during their lifetime. After cannabis, the most commonly used drug is cocaine (15.6% regular or occasional users) followed by ecstasy (13.1% regular or occasional users).

A very small proportion (1.2%) of respondents classify themselves as regular class A drug users with 17.6% of students stating they are occasional class A drug users.[3]

Class A drugs include:

Ecstasy, LSD, Cocaine, Magic Mushrooms, Heroin and Crack

Table 5.2 Other drug use

	Amphetamines		Ecstasy		LSD		Cocaine	
	N	(%)	N	(%)	N	(%)	N	(%)
Never/rarely	2,089	(90.9)	2,014	(86.6)	2,173	(96.2)	1,977	(84.3)
Occasionally	183	(8.0)	265	(11.4)	71	(3.1)	313	(13.3)
Regularly	26	(1.1)	46	(1.7)	14	(0.6)	55	(2.3)
Total	2,298	(100.0)	2,325	(100.0)	2,258	(100.0)	2,345	(100.0)
	Ketamine		Magic mushrooms		Heroin		Crack	
	N	(%)	N	(%)	N	(%)	N	(%)
Never/rarely	2,169	(95.9)	2,059	(90.1)	2,233	(98.9)	2,200	(97.6)
Occasionally	77	(3.4)	203	(8.9)	14	(0.6)	38	(1.7)
Regularly	15	(0.7)	23	(1.0)	10	(0.4)	17	(0.8)
Total	2,261	(100.0)	2,285	(100.0)	2,257	(100.0)	2,255	(100.0)

Drug use by West Sussex HE and FE students

From this survey data it is possible to establish whether a respondent has ever used a particular drug in their lifetime. The British Crime Survey[4] collects data on illicit drug use and is one of the main national sources used to monitor drug misuse in England and Wales. It is interesting to note that for all drugs except amphetamines, a higher proportion of West Sussex HE and FE students have tried each drug compared with the national average (Table 5.3). These results are surprising as other indicators suggest that the prevalence of drug use in West Sussex is below national rates.

Table 5.3 Drug use in lifetime compared to British Crime Survey data[5]

Drug	Survey data (%)	BCS 2006/07 16 to 24-yr-olds (%)
Cannabis	42.6	39.5
Cocaine	15.6	11.2
Ecstasy	13.4	10.3
Amphetamines	9.1	11.2
Magic Mushrooms	9.9	7.0
LSD	3.7	3.2
Heroin	1.0	0.7

Smoking, drinking alcohol, binge drinking and cannabis

Cannabis use is greater among students who smoke. Half of regular smokers are also current cannabis users (49.9%) compared with 6.8% of those who have never smoked. Amongst those who regularly drink alcohol, 43.9% are current cannabis users compared with 7.6% of those who rarely or never drink alcohol. There is also a clear gradient between cannabis use and binge drinking, as shown in Figure 5.4.

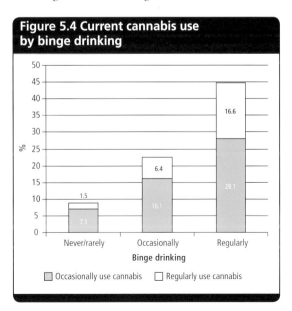

Figure 5.4 Current cannabis use by binge drinking

Table 5.4 Cocaine use by cannabis experience

Cocaine use	Cannabis experience			
	Never	Used to	Occasionally	Regularly
	(%)			
Never	98.6	73.4	67.6	37.4
Occasionally	0.8	23.0	29.2	50.9
Regularly	0.6	3.6	3.2	11.7
Total	100.0	100.0	100.0	100.0

Cannabis and other drugs

There is an association between the use of cannabis and the use of other drugs. Table 5.4 shows the use of cocaine by cannabis experience. Almost two-thirds of regular cannabis users (62.6%) also use cocaine compared with only 1.4% of those who have never used cannabis.

A similar trend can be seen with the use of cannabis and the use of other drugs.

Drug use, smoking status and general health

Smokers are more likely to report poorer health and because four-fifths of current cannabis users are also current smokers, it is important to control for this when determining health status. To separate out the effect of smoking from the effect of using cannabis three mutually exclusive categories have been created for this report: 1) those who currently do not smoke and do not use cannabis; 2) those who regularly smoke but do not currently use cannabis; and 3) those who regularly use cannabis but do not currently smoke. The proportion of these groups who report that their health is 'not good' is shown in Table 5.5.

Poor health in regular smokers (7.9%) is twice that of students who neither smoke nor use cannabis (4.1%). There is a five-fold increase in regular cannabis users reporting poor health when controlling for smoking (21.4%).

Drug use and well-being

There is a gradient between cannabis use and mental health issues (Table 5.6). Of those students who regularly use cannabis, 22.9%

Table 5.5 Proportion who report 'not good' health by cannabis and smoking status

Cannabis/smoking status	N	(%)
Neither currently smoke nor use cannabis	55	(4.1)
Regular smokers who do not currently use cannabis	27	(7.9)
Regular cannabis users who do not currently smoke	6	(21.4)

Table 5.6 Cannabis experience by well-being

Cannabis experience	Regularly stressed		Regularly depressed	
	N	(%)	N	(%)
Never/rarely	199	(13.7)	104	(7.2)
Used to	91	(18.5)	46	(9.4)
Occasionally	80	(19.9)	45	(11.2)
Regularly	43	(22.9)	33	(17.5)
Total	413	(16.3)	228	(9.0)

Table 5.7 Drug use by health and well-being

Drug use	% reporting 'not good' health		% not getting enough sleep in the past 12 months		% who have self-harmed in previous 12 months		% who have seriously considered suicide in previous 12 months	
	N	(%)	N	(%)	N	(%)	N	(%)
Never any drug	50	(4.0)	618	(49.0)	95	(7.5)	64	(5.1)
Occasional cannabis	35	(8.7)	247	(61.1)	48	(11.9)	43	(10.8)
Regular cannabis	35	(18.4)	119	(63.0)	30	(15.9)	36	(19.0)
Occasional class A	61	(13.2)	294	(63.8)	57	(12.3)	59	(12.9)
Regular class A	-	-	15	(48.4)	7	(22.6)	7	(22.6)

Data not disclosed where relates to less than 5 students.

report they regularly suffer from feeling stressed and 17.5% regularly feel depressed, compared with 13.7% and 7.2% respectively for those who have never used cannabis.

In order to look at the impact of exposure to drugs on the health and well-being of young adults, the following categories have been used: never used any drug, occasional cannabis users, regular cannabis users, occasional Class A drug users and regular Class A drug users. These categories are not mutually exclusive, for example occasional Class A drug users could also include regular cannabis users.

Table 5.7 shows respondents' drug use and their answers to questions on health and well-being. Respondents who have never tried any drug report the best well-being. Regular Class A drug users report the highest levels of self-harming and of seriously considering attempting suicide. Occasional Class A drug users tend to report better well-being than regular cannabis users.

Drugs and crime

The link between drug use and crime is well known and the survey data also shows a clear gradient between the two. Figure 5.5 shows the relationship between the use of cannabis and how often in the previous 12 months respondents had vandalised someone else's property. Over half of the students who regularly

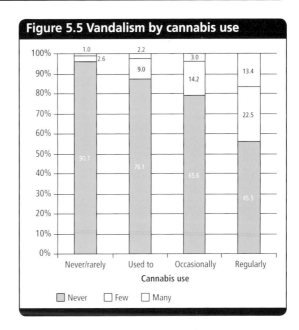

Figure 5.5 Vandalism by cannabis use

use cannabis had vandalised in the previous 12 months with more than one in ten (13.4%) doing so many times. Class A drug users also showed a similar trend in vandalism as well as in other crime variables such as being arrested and spraying graffiti.

Current drug users are more likely to be a victim of violent crime. Over a quarter (26.5%) of regular cannabis users stated they had been a victim of violent crime in the previous 12 months compared with just over one in ten (11.8%) of students who have never used any drug. (Table 5.8)

Table 5.8 Drug use by been a victim of violent crime

	N	(%)
Never used any drug	148	(11.8)
Occasional cannabis	70	(17.5)
Regular cannabis	50	(26.5)
Occasional class A	105	(22.9)
Regular class A	6	(19.4)

Table 5.9 Drug use by carried a weapon to college

	N	(%)
Never used any drug	32	(2.6)
Occasional cannabis	39	(9.8)
Regular cannabis	35	(18.7)
Occasional class A	49	(10.7)
Regular class A	8	(25.8)

When asked if they had carried a weapon to college/university over the past 12 months, 2.6% of students who have never used any drug stated they had carried a weapon compared with 18.7% of regular cannabis users and 25.8% of regular Class A drug users. (Table 5.9)

Comments

1. Cannabis is by far the most commonly used illicit drug. There are noticeable differences in use between the sexes: half of males and a third of females have tried cannabis, with 10.9% of males stating they are regular users compared with only 2.5% of females.

2. Students from natural parent families report the lowest level of current cannabis use.

3. Around one in five students have tried Class A drugs, the majority of whom are occasional users (17.6%) as opposed to regular users (1.2%).

4. For all drugs except amphetamines results from this survey show that a higher proportion of respondents had tried each drug compared with the national average in the British Crime Survey. These results are surprising as other data suggests West Sussex has lower rates than nationally; one possibility for this is that FE and HE students are a particularly high risk group. The University of Glasgow recently published 2005/06 estimates of drug use in the South East. However, due to the methodology used it is not possible to compare data from the two surveys.

5. Both cannabis and Class A drug use influence health and well-being. Cannabis users report poorer general health and greater levels of stress and feeling depressed. Students who use Class A drugs regularly are most likely to have self-harmed and seriously considered attempting suicide in the previous 12 months.

6. Current cannabis and Class A drug users are more likely to be involved in crime as well as be a victim of violent crime than previous or non-users. Regular drug users are most likely to carry a weapon with 18.7% of cannabis users and 25.8% of regular Class A drug users carrying a weapon in the last 12 months.

* Other family arrangement includes living with relatives/guardian, in a care home, or in foster care.

1 http://www.homeoffice.gov.uk/drugs/drugs-misuse/

2 http://drugs.homeoffice.gov.uk/young-people/strategy/

3 Amphetamines can be classified as either Class A (injection) or Class B (powdered). For the purpose of this analysis amphetamine use is Class B.

4 Findings from British Crime Survey, 2006/07. Home Office. Available from The Information Centre

5 Findings from British Crime Survey, 2006/07. Home Office. Available from The Information Centre

Diet and physical activity

A diet high in fruit and vegetables is associated with a decreased risk of chronic disease. A healthy diet and regular physical activity are vital ingredients of young adults' lives and contribute to good physical, emotional and mental well-being. Healthy, active young adults can have large appetites and it is important for them to eat food of high nutritional value in the form of well-balanced meals, rather than too many snacks that are rich in fat or sugar[1].

Students under 16 years of age have mandatory and regular physical education lessons at school, however this does not continue at college where participation is on a voluntary basis.

Diet

When questioned about their diet, 4.2% of students described themselves as vegetarian and 3.3% as vegan. More females (6.4%) are vegetarian than males (2.6%), while more males (4.8%) are vegan than females (1.5%). There is little variation by age.

More than one in ten students consume the recommended 5 or more portions of fruit and vegetables a day with little difference between the sexes (see Table 6.1).

Eating fruit and vegetables is widely accepted to be an important part of a balanced diet. Students living in other* family arrangements (10.9%) were the most likely to consume no fruit or vegetables, compared with those from natural parent (5.8%), parent and partner (4.7%), stepparent (6.6%) and single parent (7.9%) families.

Students were asked a series of questions on the frequency with which they ate foods associated with high fats and sugars. Male and female students gave similar answers on the consumption of sweets and chocolate with almost two-thirds consuming them at least once a day. However, more males (48.3%) than females (39.6%) consume fast food at least once a day. This trend is repeated with fizzy drinks: males are far more likely to consume fizzy drinks than females (61.4% and 39.5% respectively) (see Figure 6.1).

Table 6.1 Fruit and vegetables by sex		Male		Female		Total	
		N	(%)	N	(%)	N	(%)
Portions of fruit and vegetables eaten per day	0	134	(9.0)	37	(3.5)	171	(6.7)
	1	294	(19.7)	148	(13.8)	442	(17.2)
	2	372	(24.9)	266	(24.9)	638	(24.9)
	3	372	(24.9)	292	(27.3)	664	(25.9)
	4	173	(11.6)	163	(15.2)	336	(13.1)
	5	151	(10.1)	163	(15.2)	314	(12.2)
	Total	1496	(100.0)	1069	(100.0)	2565	(100.0)

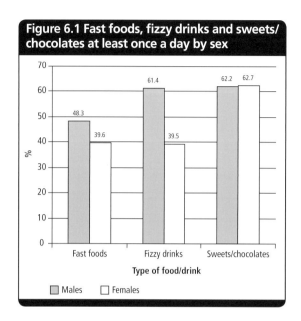

Figure 6.1 Fast foods, fizzy drinks and sweets/chocolates at least once a day by sex

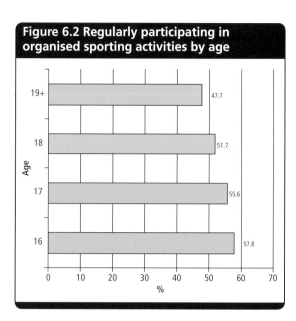

Figure 6.2 Regularly participating in organised sporting activities by age

Physical Activity

Respondents were asked questions on physical activities and self-perceived fitness. Table 6.2 shows that while one in ten students declared themselves 'very fit', males (13.1%) were more than twice as likely as females (5.6%) to do so. More females (36.2%) than males (21.9%) stated themselves unfit, while similar proportions of both sexes declared themselves 'very unfit' (2.2% males, 2.8% females).

As all respondents are attending colleges where sporting activities can be accessed, they were asked 'whether over the past year they have regularly participated in organised sporting activities.'

Males (59.7%) are more likely to have regularly participated in sporting activities than females (40.3%).

Regular participation in organised sporting activities decreases slightly with age. Of those aged 16, 57.8% have regularly participated in sports compared with 47.7% of those aged 19 or over (see Figure 6.2).

In order to ascertain the level of physical activity undertaken, students were asked:

In an average week, how many times do you take part in physical activity for 30 minutes or more so that you are out of breath?

Table 6.2 Perceived physical fitness by sex

	Male		Female		Total	
	N	(%)	N	(%)	N	(%)
Very fit	199	(13.1)	60	(5.6)	259	(10.0)
Fit	957	(62.9	598	(55.4)	1555	(59.8)
Unfit	333	(21.9)	391	(36.2)	724	(27.8)
Very unfit	33	(2.2)	30	(2.8)	63	(2.4)
Total	1522	(100.0)	1079	(100.0)	2601	(100.0)

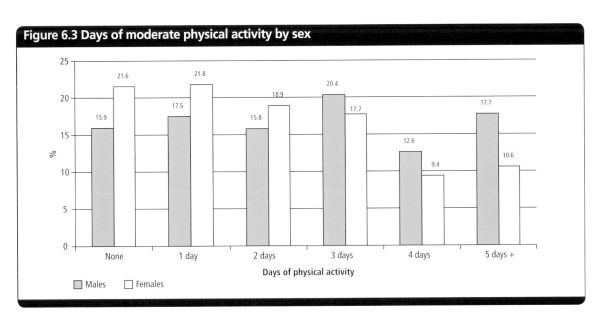

Figure 6.3 Days of moderate physical activity by sex

Figure 6.3 shows that males tend to be more physically active than females, with the largest difference seen in those who participate 5 days or more: 10.6% of females and 17.7% of males. Just less than one in five students do not participate at all (21.6% of females and 15.9% of males).

As seen with organised sporting activities, the frequency of participation in physical activity decreases with age. Around 17% of under 19s do not take part in physical activity compared with nearly a quarter (24.5%) of those aged 19 years or over.

Physical activity and health

When questioned about their health, 11.5% of students who do no physical activity perceived their health status as not good, compared with 5.0% of those who exercise for three days or more.

Sport England 'Active People' survey

The Sport England 'Active People' 2006 survey was undertaken using a random sample of young people over 16-years-old. Sport England reported that 32.7% of 16 to 24-year-olds did not take part in any moderate physical activity in an average week while 33.6% of respondents took part at least three times a week.

This survey found that 18.3% of students did not participate in any moderate physical activity in an average week while 35.4% participated at least three times a week. The 'Active People' survey was a representative sample of the 16 to 24-year-old population, whereas this survey only questioned students in Further and Higher Education and therefore is not necessarily a representative sample of the age group in West Sussex.

Physical activity and well-being

Figure 6.4 shows the proportions of males and females who regularly feel depressed by the number of days of moderate physical activity. Among male students there is a gradient: more moderate physical activity means less depression. For example, among those who do no physical activity 10% regularly feel depressed compared with around 4% of those who exercise for three or four days per week. Among females there is a different picture, with highest rates of regular depression observed among those who participate in physical activity on five days or more (19.5%).

There is no discernable relationship between the number of days a student participates in moderate physical activity and the frequency with which they feel regularly stressed.

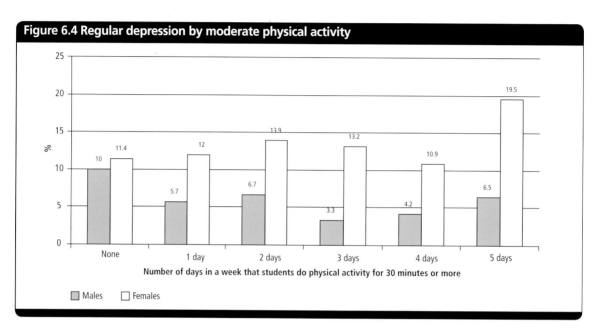

Figure 6.4 Regular depression by moderate physical activity

Number of days in a week that students do physical activity for 30 minutes or more

Males Females

Male students who regularly participate in organised sporting activities are less likely to have regularly felt depressed (4.8%) than those who have not (8.8%). Among female students the rate of feeling depressed was similar whether they regularly participated in organised sporting activities or not (12.8% v 13.4%).

Comments

1. This survey shows that 12.2% of students consume the recommended 5 or more portions of fruit and vegetables a day. The results almost mirror the findings of the recent 'Lifestyles of 14 to 15-year-olds' report which found that 13% of pupils eat '5 a day'. Nevertheless, the fact that just under half of the students consume less than 3 portions of fruit and vegetables suggests that there is a need to promote to this age group the importance of a healthy, balanced diet.

2. The majority of students consume fast foods, fizzy drinks and sweets and chocolate at least once a day. While this is probably a part of student life, it is important to encourage students to eat a balanced diet.

3. Participation in physical activity decreases with age. This is further supported when the results are compared with the 'Lifestyles of 14 to 15-year-olds' in West Sussex 2007, which found that 3% of boys and 6% of girls participated in no moderate physical activity compared with 15.9% of males and 21.6% of females in the 16 to 24-year-old age range[2].

4. A surprising finding was the relationship between moderate physical activity and feelings of depression. While among male students, those who do more physical activity tend to have lower rates of depression, among female students there was no discernable association and we were surprised to find that the highest rates of depression are among the most physically active female students.

* Other family arrangement includes living with relatives/guardian, in a care home, or in foster care.

[1] http://www.eatwell.gov.uk/agesandstages/children/yourteen/

[2] Lifestyles of 14 to 15-year-olds in West Sussex 2007, West Sussex PCT and West Sussex County Council July 2007.

Obesity

Being overweight and obese is on the increase, with the country facing what is being called an 'obesity epidemic'. The Department of Health estimates that obesity is responsible for over 9,000 premature deaths a year in England[1]. Being overweight is a risk factor for many chronic diseases and can have an impact on mental health. As young people move into adulthood it is important that they are aware they are able to make lifestyle choices to prevent and manage excess weight and obesity.

The students were asked to give both their height and weight. It is worth noting that these are self-reported and that studies have shown individuals tend to over-estimate their height and under-estimate their weight.

Height

Over four-fifths of respondents (84.2%) gave their height. The average height for males is 5ft 11inches and for females is 5ft 5inches, both taller than the national average for 16 to 24-year-olds (5ft 9.5 for males, 5ft 4.5 for females)[2]. There is very little difference in height between females of different ages, and for males those aged 16-years-old are on average an inch shorter than those aged 17 years or over.

National height and weight data comes from the Health Survey for England 2006 which is a measured survey. The data in this survey is self-reported.

Weight

Three-quarters of students (75.1%) gave their weight with more males (81.7%) providing their weight than females (66.6%). The average weight for males is 11st 2lbs and for females it is 9st 1lb. Both sexes are lighter on average than nationally; in England the average is 11st 12lbs

for males and 10st 2lbs for females. For both sexes, 19-year-olds are approximately a stone heavier than 16-year-olds.

Self-perception of weight

The students were asked to put themselves into one of 5 categories with regard to their weight. Figure 7.1 shows that the more overweight individuals perceive themselves to be, the less likely they are to give their weight, particularly amongst females.

Around two-thirds of students (65.2%) perceive themselves to be of normal weight with a higher proportion of females than males classifying themselves as overweight (31.9% and 22.1% respectively). One in ten males consider themselves to be underweight (11.1%) compared with only 5.3% of females (Table 7.1).

BMI

Body Mass Index (BMI) is a standard measure used to define whether an individual is overweight or not. It is a ratio comparing weight to height with standard cut offs used to classify whether an adult is overweight or obese. In children (under 18s) it is not as straight forward and adjustments need to be made to allow for growth and development. Reference charts are used with classifications based on percentiles for the

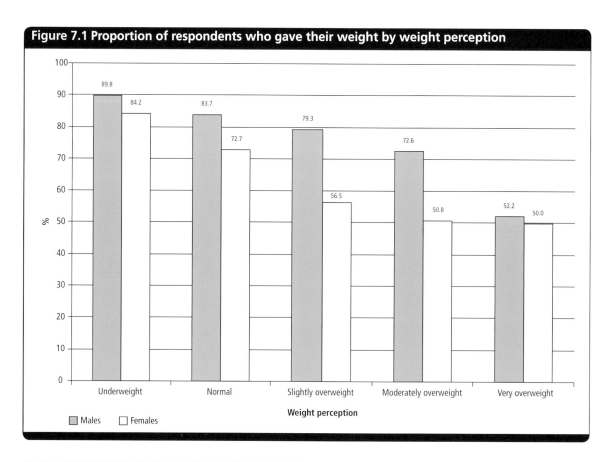

Figure 7.1 Proportion of respondents who gave their weight by weight perception

Table 7.1 Perceived weight by sex

	Male		Female		All	
	N	(%)	N	(%)	N	(%)
Underweight	167	(11.1)	57	(5.3)	224	(8.7)
Normal	1,007	(66.8)	674	(62.8)	1,681	(65.2)
Slightly overweight	237	(15.7)	255	(23.8)	492	(19.1)
Moderately overweight	73	(4.8)	63	(5.9)	136	(5.3)
Very overweight	23	(1.5)	24	(2.2)	47	(1.8)
Total	1,507	(100.0)	1,073	(100.0)	2,580	(100.0)

appropriate age and sex. The UK 1990 reference charts are commonly used with those over the 91st percentile classified as overweight and those over the 98th percentile classified as obese. Individuals who fall below the 91st percentile are classed as either normal or underweight.

$$\frac{\text{Weight (kg)}}{\text{Height (m}^2)} = \text{BMI (kg/m}^2)$$

Table 7.2 Mean BMI by age and sex		
Age	Males	Females
16	21.9	21.0
17	21.9	21.2
18	22.0	21.4
19	23.1	22.1
20	23.5	21.3

From the data collected in the survey 1,841 respondents (68.9%) provided both their height and weight allowing BMI to be calculated. The mean BMI for males is 22.3 and for females 21.4. Table 7.2 shows the mean BMI by age and sex.

Adult BMI classifications:

<18.5 underweight

18.5 - 24.9 normal

25.0 – 29.9 overweight

30+ obese

For those aged 18 or over the standard adult cut offs were used to classify whether the students were overweight or not; for those under 18 years of age, the 1990 UK reference charts were used. There is a noticeable difference between the sexes with 13.9% of males classified as overweight and 7.7% as obese, compared with 7.3% and 3.9% of females respectively (see Table 7.3). Males are twice as likely (21.6%) to be overweight or obese as females (11.2%), although it is important to note that self-perceived overweight females are less likely to provide their weight.

From the data in this survey, analysis of mean BMI shows that there is no clear relationship between an individual's BMI and their fruit and vegetable consumption, or between BMI and their consumption of certain foods high in sugar and fat (sweets or chocolate, fast foods and fizzy drinks). There is no relationship between BMI and levels of physical activity and participation in organised sport. For example, those who participate in organised sport have a mean BMI of 22.2 (95% CI 21.9-22.4) compared with 21.8 (95% CI 21.5-22.0) for those who do not do any organised sporting activities.

Students who watch TV for more than two hours a day have a higher BMI on average than those who watch less (22.5, 95% CI 22.1-22.8 and 21.6, 95% CI 21.4-21.9 respectively).

Students who are classified as obese are twice as likely (23.5%) to be a victim of bullying as those who are normal or overweight (10.7%). This is even more noticeable from the self-perception weight categories with those who consider themselves very overweight four times more likely to be a victim of bullying compared with those who consider themselves to be of normal weight (40.4% and 10.4% respectively).

Table 7.3 BMI by sex	Males		Females		All	
	N	(%)	N	(%)	N	(%)
Normal/underweight	904	(78.4)	611	(988.8)	1,515	(82.3)
Overweight	160	(13.9)	50	(7.3)	210	(11.4)
Obese	89	(7.7)	27	(3.9)	116	(6.3)
Total	1,153	(100)	688	(100)	1,841	(100)

Comments

1. Both males and females are taller and lighter than the national average for 16 to 24-year-olds (note that individuals tend to underestimate self-reported weight and over estimate self-reported height).

2. As expected, those who perceive themselves to be overweight are less likely to provide details on their weight, with noticeable differences between the sexes. Of those who perceive themselves to be overweight, 76.0% of males gave their weight compared with only 55.0% of females. If those who did not give their weight but consider themselves to be either moderately or very overweight are included, the prevalence of being overweight (including obese) decreases to 19.8% for males, with only a very small increase to 11.6% for females.

3. Males are twice as likely as females to be classified as overweight or obese (21.6% and 11.2% respectively). Analysis of students' weight perception reveals that a much higher proportion of females consider themselves as overweight or obese (31.9%) than males where the proportion remains the same (22.0%).

4. Following national trends, higher proportions of those aged 16 to 24-years-old are either overweight or obese (21.6% for males and 11.2% for females) compared with 14 and 15-year-olds in West Sussex (16% boys and 9% girls)[3].

5. Over one in ten males consider themselves to be underweight (11.1%). Body image can be just as much an issue for males as they aspire to become more muscular and toned. For males aged 18 years or over who perceive themselves to be underweight, less than half (43.1%) are actually classified as underweight according to their BMI.

6. Preventing and managing obesity and excess weight is a lifestyle issue requiring environmental and behavioural changes. Many barriers to lifestyle changes exist and it is important to understand these for the 16 to 24-year-old age group in order to be able to address the rising levels of those who are overweight and obese.

[1] http://www.dh.gov.uk/en/Policyandguidance/Healthandsocialcaretopics/Obesity/index.htm

[2] Health Survey for England, 2006 16 to 24-year-olds

[3] Lifestyles of 14 to 15-year-olds in West Sussex 2007, West Sussex PCT and West Sussex County Council July 2007

Emotional health and well-being

"Mental health is as important to an individual as good physical health. Mental health influences how we feel, perceive, think, communicate and understand. Without good mental health, people can be unable to fulfil their full potential or play an active part in everyday life." [1]

The mental health of young adults is an important factor in their overall well-being. The foundations for good mental well-being are laid in childhood and depend to a great extent on the quality of the emotional and social environment provided by parents, families, teachers and peers. The transition from adolescence to young adulthood can be a challenging time. Major decisions affecting personal relationships, independent living, family and working life are made during this period and pressure can therefore be felt from many different angles.

Making the adjustment to adult life depends on a range of factors. These include the current and past family situation, social circumstances, training, employment and housing opportunities, as well as the quality and amount of support and encouragement and the state of a young person's mental health[2]. Health and well-being can be affected by these pressures and by the period of

Risk factors for feeling depressed include family discord, bullying, physical, sexual or emotional abuse, drug and alcohol use, or a history of parental depression.[3]

change and as mental health problems in young people have been found to be a clear predictor of problems in adulthood, it is essential to treat them early.

Suffering from stress and feeling depressed

When students were asked how often they felt depressed (Table 8.1), around one in ten (9.2%) reported regularly feeling depressed, with just over twice as many females (13.2%) as males (6.4%) admitting they suffered. Nearly half of the students (46.5%) reported never or rarely feeling depressed, which included 53.8% of males and 36.4% of females. Results were consistent across the different age groups.

Table 8.1 Feeling depressed by sex	Male		Female		All	
	N	(%)	N	(%)	N	(%)
Never/rarely	817	(53.8)	396	(36.4)	1,213	(46.5)
Occasionally	605	(39.8)	548	(50.4)	1,153	(44.2)
Regularly	97	(6.4)	144	(13.2)	241	(9.2)
Total	1,519	(100.0)	1,088	(100.0)	2,607	(100.0)

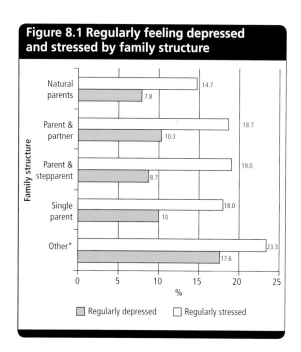

Figure 8.1 Regularly feeling depressed and stressed by family structure

Legend: Regularly depressed / Regularly stressed

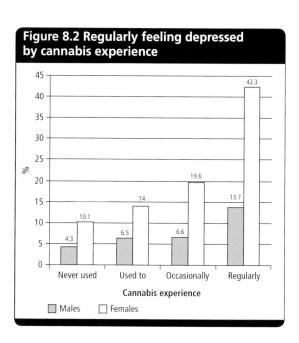

Figure 8.2 Regularly feeling depressed by cannabis experience

Legend: Males / Females

Students living with both natural parents are the least likely to regularly feel depressed (7.8%) whilst those living in other* family arrangements were the highest (17.6%).

Feeling stressed

The information in Table 8.2 shows that females are more than twice as likely to report regularly feeling stressed (24.1%) as males (11.2%). Results were consistent across the different age groups.

Students living in other* family arrangements reported the highest incidence of stress (23.3%),

compared with those living in parent and stepparent (19.0%), parent and partner (18.7%), single parent (18.0%) and natural parent families (14.7%).

Depression, stress and cannabis

There is an association between cannabis experience and regular feelings of depression, as shown in Figure 8.2. Females who regularly use cannabis are four times more likely to feel depressed than those who have never used it. Males who are regular cannabis users are three times more likely to feel depressed than those who have never used it.

Table 8.2 Feeling stressed by sex

	Male		Female		All	
	N	(%)	N	(%)	N	(%)
Never/rarely	679	(44.7)	271	(24.7)	950	(36.4)
Occasionally	669	(44.1)	560	(51.1)	1,229	(47.0)
Regularly	170	(11.2)	264	(24.1)	434	(16.6)
Total	1,518	(100.0)	1,095	(100.0)	2,613	(100.0)

Getting enough sleep

Students were asked the question:

In the past 12 months, on average have you felt like you get enough sleep to ensure that you can concentrate on your studies?

Slightly more females (59.5%) reported that they did not have enough sleep to concentrate compared with 52.6% of males. Perhaps unsurprisingly, those who regularly feel depressed are more likely to get insufficient sleep (77.4%) compared with those who occasionally (59.7%) and never (47.0%) feel depressed.

Worrying about failing your course

To the question:

How much do you worry about failing your course?

29.2% of students responded that they worried a lot, just over half (51.2%) said they worried a little and 19.6% did not worry at all. More females (34.9%) than males (25.1%) stated that they worried a lot about failing their course.

Work interfering with studies

With just under three-quarters of students in some form of employment (see Section 2), almost a quarter (23.0%) felt that their work was interfering with their studies. Students who felt that this was the case were more likely to be regularly feeling depressed (13.9%) and stressed (26.0%) than those who did not feel work affected their studies (7.3% and 13.9% respectively).

Self-harmed over the past 12 months

Self-harm, or self-injury, describes a wide range of ways in which people deliberately hurt or injure themselves. Female students are more likely to have self-harmed (12.9%) than males

(6.4%) in the past 12 months. The proportion of students who have self-harmed over the past year decreases with age: twice the proportion of 16 and 17-year-olds (11.1%) have self-harmed compared with those aged 19 or over (5.5%).

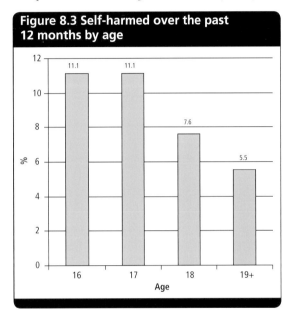

Figure 8.3 Self-harmed over the past 12 months by age

Students living in other* family arrangements are the most likely to have self-harmed (16.7%) over the past 12 months (Figure 8.4).

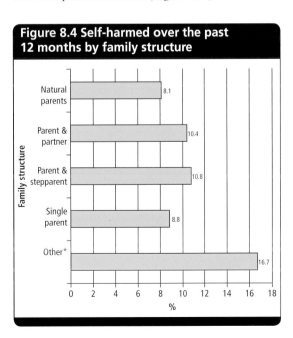

Figure 8.4 Self-harmed over the past 12 months by family structure

Self-harm and feeling depressed

As expected there is a strong relationship between self-harm and feelings of depression. Only 2.4% of students who never feel depressed have self-harmed over the past 12 months, compared with 9.4% of those who occasionally and 42.7% of those who regularly feel depressed.

Self-harm and cannabis use

Figure 8.5 shows a clear gradient between use of cannabis and self-harm over the past 12 months. Among females there is a marked gradient with regular users of cannabis (34.6%) being three times more likely to have self-harmed than those who have never used (10.6%). Among male students, regular uses (13.0%) are three times more likely to self-harm compared to those who have never used (4.2%).

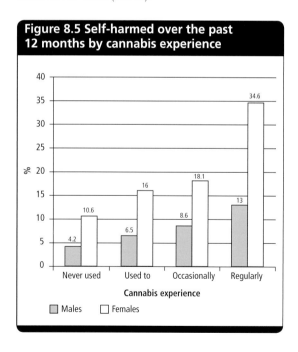

Figure 8.5 Self-harmed over the past 12 months by cannabis experience

Seriously contemplated suicide over the past 12 months

In 2004 suicide accounted for one-fifth of all deaths amongst young adults aged 15 to 24.[4] Across all age groups, the male suicide rate is higher than the female suicide rate and currently men are almost three times more likely than women to die from committing suicide. Young women aged between 15 and 19 years are more likely to attempt suicide than young men, however, young men are much more likely to die as a result of their suicide attempt.[5] The suicide rate in males aged under 25 has doubled since 1985, listing them second only to men in the 25-44 age range.

When students were asked if they had seriously contemplated suicide over the last 12 months, 8.2% said they had, with females (9.8%) more likely to report they had seriously considered suicide than males (7.0%).

There is a variation with the age of female students: those under 19 have a higher rate of contemplating suicide (10.5%) than those over 19-years-old (7.3%). Among males there is little difference by age: the rate is 7.0% and 6.4% among under and over 19s respectively.

Students living in other* family arrangements are the most likely to seriously have considered suicide (23.5%) compared with those from single parent (8.3%), parent and partner (6.7%), natural parent (6.6%) and parent and stepparent (6.1%) families.

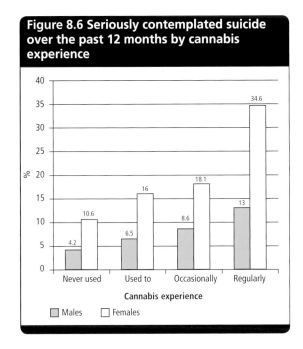

Figure 8.6 Seriously contemplated suicide over the past 12 months by cannabis experience

Cannabis experience and suicide

Regular cannabis users are three times more likely (19.0%) to have seriously contemplated suicide then those who have never used cannabis (5.7%) and nearly twice as likely as those who only use cannabis occasionally (10.8%) (Figure 8.6).

Comments

1. Those living in other* family arrangements are at most risk of regularly feeling stressed and depressed. Regular cannabis use is associated with a higher incidence of feeling depressed, of self-harm and of seriously contemplating suicide. These findings have an important health promotion message.

2. Females are less likely than males to get sufficient sleep in order to concentrate on their studies. Those living in single parent households are the highest risk family group for insufficient sleep.

3. Just over one in ten females have self-harmed over the past 12 months, and females are twice as likely as males to have self-harmed. Students aged 16 to 17-years-old are twice as likely to have self-harmed as those aged 19 or over.

4. Self-harming is associated with regularly feeling depressed. Self-harm may be part of coping with a specific problem and can stop once the problem is resolved or it might be used for years whenever certain pressures or feelings arise. The National Inquiry into self-harm among young adults aged 11 to 25-years-old has found that one in 15 young adults has self-harmed.[6] A recent study found that four times more adolescent females self-harmed than adolescent males.[7]

5. Slightly more females than males have seriously contemplated suicide over the past 12 months. Those living in other* family arrangements and those who regularly use cannabis are associated with higher levels of suicidal feelings.

* Other family arrangement includes living with relatives/guardian, in a care home, or in foster care.

[1] Our Healthier Nation White Paper, Department of Health, July 1999

[2] http://www.youngminds.org.uk/adolescentpolicy/

[3] Depression in children and young people, Identification and management in primary, community and secondary care, NICE Sept 2005.

[4] MIND website

[5] http://www.mind.org.uk/Information/Factsheets/Suicide/#_ftn14

[6] Truth Hurts, Mental Health Foundation/Camelot Foundation, 2006

[7] Samaritans, 2003

Bullying

While bullying at school receives a lot of publicity, less is known about bullying among young adults attending college. However, initial focus groups with college students for this survey suggested that it was a prominent issue for them.

Although definitions can vary, bullying can be described as when a person or group of people deliberately and persistently target someone else in order to hurt. The actions can be verbal, physical or psychological.[1] Social research indicates a power imbalance between the victim and the aggressor.

Victims of bullying can suffer anxiousness, low self-esteem and isolation. Bullying can lead to a culture of intimidation and fear in the educational environment.[2]

Victims of bullying

Overall 12.3 % of students reported that they had been bullied over the past year. Table 9.1, which presents bullying by age, shows an age gradient: 16.1% of 16-year-olds reported that they have been bullied over the past year compared with 8.6% of those aged 20 and over. There was also a difference by sex with 14.5% of females saying that they had been bullied compared with 10.6% of males. The group most susceptible to bullying was females aged 16 and 17 (18.7% and 15.8% respectively).

Bullying and family structure

Students living in other* family arrangements were the group most likely to be victims of bullying (24.6%), followed by those from stepparent (18.3%) and parent and partner families (13.1%).

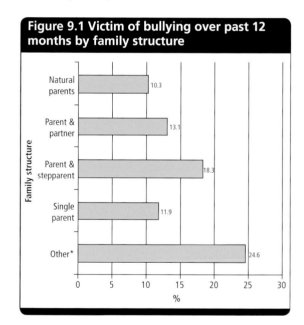

Figure 9.1 Victim of bullying over past 12 months by family structure

Family structure	%
Natural parents	10.3
Parent & partner	13.1
Parent & stepparent	18.3
Single parent	11.9
Other*	24.6

Table 9.1 Victim of bullying over past 12 months by age						
Age	Yes		No		All	
	N	(%)	N	(%)	N	(%)
16	68	(16.1)	355	(83.9)	423	(100.0)
17	142	(13.3)	925	(86.7)	1067	(100.0)
18	66	(11.7)	498	(88.3)	564	(100.0)
19	18	(7.6)	220	(92.4)	238	(100.0)
20	26	(8.6)	277	(91.4)	303	(100.0)
Total	320	(12.3)	2275	(87.7)	2595	(100.0)

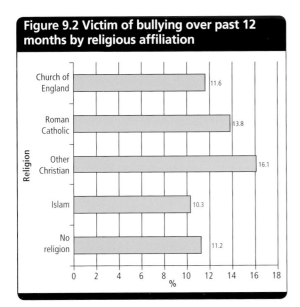

Figure 9.2 Victim of bullying over past 12 months by religious affiliation

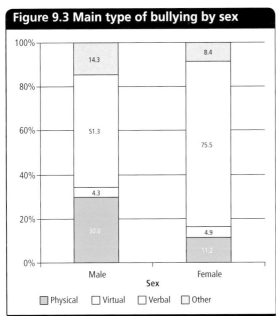

Figure 9.3 Main type of bullying by sex

Students who had been victims of bullying were asked what type of bullying they had experienced; their answers are shown in Figure 9.3. Males and females reported similar types of bullying, with verbal bullying being the most common for both. Physical bullying is more likely to be experienced by males (30.0%) than females (11.2%). It is important to note the relatively new presence of virtual bullying which has become a factor with the improved Internet access and the increased use of mobile phones in the last few years.

The freedom with which students feel they are able to report bullying is an important indicator of how supported students feel and it can have an impact on the outcome of the bullying. Students were asked to grade the degree to which they agreed with the statement:

I feel encouraged to report bullying and aggression

Females were slightly more likely to agree (81.7%) than males (70.2%). The age of students had little impact on the response to this question.

Place of bullying

Over half of the students who had been bullied reported being bullied at college. While 18.8% reported bullying in 'other' places, 9.5% reported bullying on the way to either college or school and 6.6% said it took place at work. Figure 9.4 shows the results by sex. A larger proportion of females were bullied at college (64.0%) than males (46.9%).

Bullying and emotional well-being

The effect of being bullied can be harmful to the emotional well-being of students. Figure 9.5 shows that those who have been bullied over 12 months are over three times more likely to regularly feel depressed (24.1%) than those who have not (7.2%). Victims of bullying are also far more likely to regularly feel stressed.

Bullying and religion

There is a relationship between religious affiliation and bullying. The group most likely to be victims of bullying were Other Christians (16.1%) and Roman Catholics (13.8%) as shown in Figure 9.2. The group who attended religious services weekly are the most likely to be bullied (21.7%), followed by those who attend monthly (16.0%) and those who attended yearly or less often (12.5%).

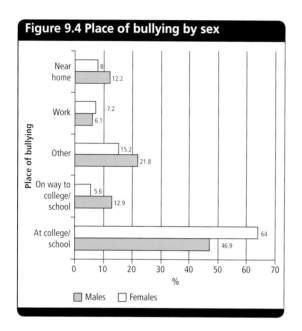

Figure 9.4 Place of bullying by sex

Place of bullying / %

- Near home: 8 (Females), 12.2 (Males)
- Work: 7.2 (Females), 6.1 (Males)
- Other: 15.2 (Females), 21.8 (Males)
- On way to college/school: 5.6 (Females), 12.9 (Males)
- At college/school: 64 (Females), 46.9 (Males)

☐ Males ☐ Females

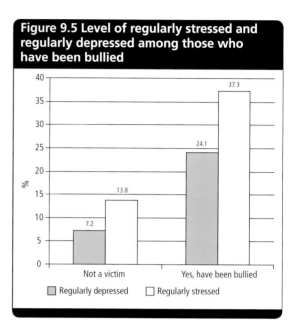

Figure 9.5 Level of regularly stressed and regularly depressed among those who have been bullied

%

- Not a victim: 7.2 (Regularly depressed), 13.8 (Regularly stressed)
- Yes, have been bullied: 24.1 (Regularly depressed), 37.3 (Regularly stressed)

☐ Regularly depressed ☐ Regularly stressed

Bullying and self-harm

Those who have been bullied are five times more likely to have self-harmed over the past year (29.7%) than those who have not (6.4%). They are also nearly five times (25.4%) more likely to have seriously contemplated suicide than those who have not been bullied over the past year (5.8%).

Bullying and cannabis

Students who have been bullied are more likely to be regular cannabis users (10.6%) than those who have not been bullied (7.1%).

Comments

1. Around one in eight students reported that they had been victims of bullying over the past year. Bullying was more common among the younger students and among females. Highest rates are reported among female students aged under 18. Students who tended to be religious, as measured by the question on religious observance, were more likely to be victims of bullying.

2. Verbal bullying is the most prevalent type of bullying with especially high rates among females. Physical bullying is more common among males. The presence of virtual bullying should also be acknowledged.

3. It is encouraging to see that around three-quarters of students feel that they are supported to report bullying.

4. A higher proportion of females are victims of bullying at college than males, while more males are bullied near their homes.

5. The destructive nature of bullying is clearly demonstrated by the victims' high levels of regularly feeling depressed and stressed. Even more worrying is the finding that victims of bullying are five times more likely to self-harm and to seriously contemplate suicide than students who have not been bullied.

* Other family arrangement includes living with relatives/guardian, in a care home, or in foster care.

[1] http://portal.king-edmund.com/ke-www/information/Bullying%20Policy.pdf

[2] Home Office Fear of Crime Team (2006), Crime reduction toolkits: Fear of crime: Youth.

Crime and safety

Much discussion about young adults centres on crime and safety with recent violent crime, particularly between inner city gangs, making regular headlines. While young adults, particularly males, are often associated with being the perpetrators of crime, they are also more likely than older people to be the victims of crime[1]. With this in mind students were asked a range of questions about both committing a crime and being the victim of crime which included the areas of being arrested, vandalism and graffiti, theft, carrying a weapon and the sensitive topic of domestic violence. Also included in this section are the results from questions on road safety.

Been arrested

Students were asked if they had been arrested in the past 12 months. Around one in five (22.1%) of males had been arrested and half of those more than once. A lower proportion of females, one in 20 (4.8%), had been arrested. Students residing with both natural parents were the least likely to have been arrested (12.8%) and those living in other* family arrangements were the most likely (24.0%) as can be seen in Figure 10.1. Respondents from other* family arrangements are also the most likely to have been arrested many times.

Students with no religion were more likely to have been arrested over the past year (17.1%) than students who are affiliated to any of the Christian religions (10.0%).

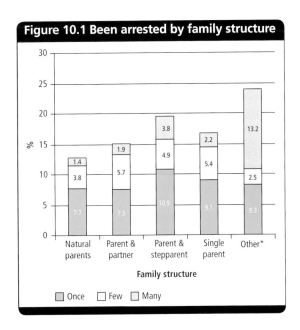

Figure 10.1 Been arrested by family structure

Table 10.1 Been arrested by sex						
	Male		Female		All	
	N	(%)	N	(%)	N	(%)
Never	1176	(77.9)	1037	(95.3)	2213	(85.2)
Once	170	(11.3)	42	(3.9)	212	(8.2)
Few/many	163	(10.8)	9	(0.8)	172	(6.6)
Total	1509	(100)	1088	(100)	2597	(100)

Vandalism and graffiti in the past 12 months

When asked if they had vandalised somebody else's property over the past 12 months, over a quarter (28.0%) of male students had vandalised somebody else's property at least once compared with 8.2% of females. Only 3.0% of females had vandalised somebody else's property a 'few or many times' compared with 15.0% of males. There was little variation across the age groups. Students who live with both parents are the least likely to have vandalised (18.0%) and those living with parent and partner families are the most likely (25.5%) (Figure 10.2).

The type of student writing or spraying graffiti, perhaps unsurprisingly, is similar to the type who commits vandalism. Just over one in ten students have sprayed graffiti over the past year, with a higher proportion of males (15.3%) than females (5.0%) doing so (Figure 10.2).

Crime and drugs

One in three of those who currently use cannabis (regular and occasional users) have been arrested compared with over one in 20 of those who have never used cannabis. Figure

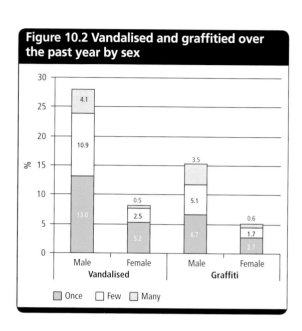

Figure 10.2 Vandalised and graffitied over the past year by sex

10.3 shows the relationship between the cannabis experience and the frequency of being arrested in the past 12 months. Half of regular cannabis users have been arrested in the last year and 32% of these have been arrested a few or many times compared with 1.6% of those who have never used cannabis. A quarter of occasional cannabis users have been arrested and 11.9% a few or many times.

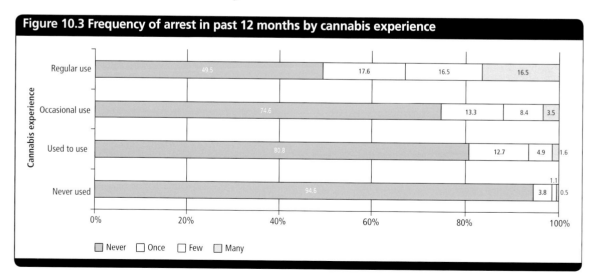

Figure 10.3 Frequency of arrest in past 12 months by cannabis experience

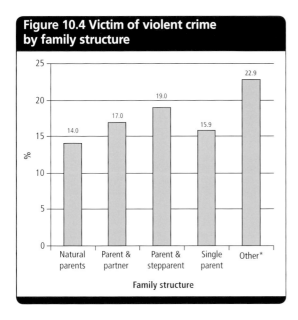

Figure 10.4 Victim of violent crime by family structure

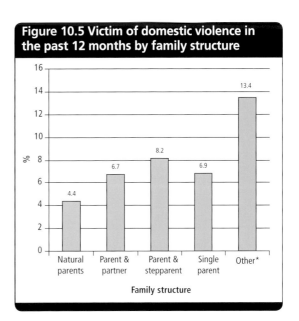

Figure 10.5 Victim of domestic violence in the past 12 months by family structure

Victims of theft

Students were asked the following question about theft:

In the past 12 months, have you ever had items such as cash, bicycle, MP3 player, mobile phone or other electrical equipment stolen?

Just under a quarter of all students reported that they had had something stolen in the past year. A larger proportion of males (25.0%) than females (17.8%) reported being a victim of theft however there is little variation across the age groups.

Students who live with both natural parents (20.1%) have the lowest incidence of being a victim of theft along with those in stepparent families (20.1%). Students from parent and partner (29.2%) and living in other* family arrangements (35.8%) are the most likely to have been a victim of theft.

Victims of violent crime

When asked if they had been a victim of violent crime over the past 12 months, 15.7% of students reported that they had been a victim. The results of this survey are supported by national trends: more males (17.8%) than females (12.9%) have been victims.

Students living with natural parents are the least likely to have been a victim of violent crime (14.0%), whereas the other* (22.9%) and stepparent (19.0%) family groups are the most likely (Figure 10.4).

Domestic violence

The survey included two questions on domestic violence. The first asked if respondents had been a victim of domestic violence over the past year and the second if they had witnessed domestic violence over the past year.

Just over one in twenty students (6.1%) had been a victim of domestic violence, with little difference between the sexes whereas more males (16.5%) than females (12.6%) had witnessed domestic violence.

Students who live in other* family arrangements are more likely (13.4%) to have been a victim of domestic violence and to have witnessed domestic violence (27.7%) than the rest of the family groupings. Students from natural parent families are the least likely (4.4%) to have suffered this violence and the least likely to have witnessed it (11.1%).

Carried a weapon to college

Students were asked if they had carried a weapon to college in the past year. Males were nearly four times more likely to have carried a weapon to college than females (8.3% and 2.0% respectively). Students from natural parent families (4.9%) are the least likely to have carried a weapon to college while those from other* family structures are the most likely (9.2%).

Those students who have carried a weapon to college are twice as likely (69.1%) to regularly watch films, games and videos that include explicit violence as those who do not regularly watch (33.5%) this type of entertainment.

Road Safety

Respondents were asked a series of questions on their behaviour as drivers of vehicles and their experiences as passengers in a car.

A higher proportion of males (14.1%) than females (4.1%) have points on their vehicle licence. Over one in ten males and just 2.3% of females said they regularly drove while on their mobile phones.

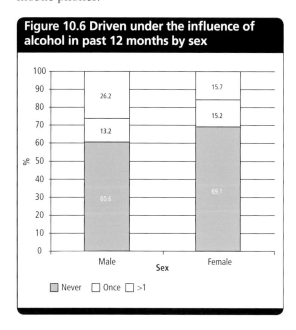

Figure 10.6 Driven under the influence of alcohol in past 12 months by sex

Never	Once	>1

Table 10.2 Driven under the influence of drugs over the past 12 months by sex

Driven under the influence of drugs over the past 12 months	Sex	
	Male	Female
	%	
Never	77.3	93.9
Once	7.0	2.5
More than once	15.8	3.6
Total	100.0	100.0

When asked how often they had driven under the influence of drugs or alcohol, nine out of ten females said they had never driven under the influence of alcohol compared to seven out of ten males. Over one in ten males had driven under the influence of alcohol more than once.

More males (22.8%) than females (6.1%) have driven under the influence of drugs with over one in ten males doing so more than once (Table 10.2).

Nearly a third of females (30.9%) and two-fifths of males (39.4%) have been a passenger in a car in the last 12 months where the driver was under the influence of alcohol or illegal drugs. Around a quarter of males and 15.8% of females have been in this situation more than once.

Attitude to driving

Students were asked to express their level of agreement or disagreement with three statements, as shown in Figure 10.7. The most noticeable finding was the large difference in attitude between male and female students. More female students (74.0%) than male students (62.6%) strongly agree that they always wear a seat belt. Females (61.2%) were also far more likely than males (29.1%) to disagree with the statement that they occasionally take risks to impress friends in the car. Males were more likely than females to agree that it is OK to speed if traffic conditions allow it (44.3% males, 25.3% females).

Figure 10.7 Attitude to driving a motor vehicle by sex

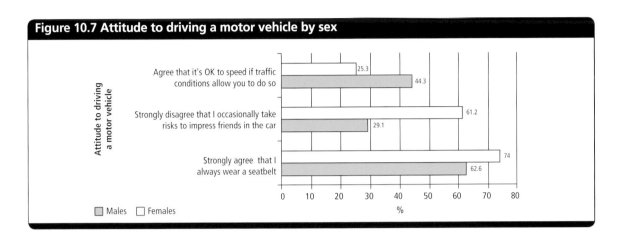

Males ☐ Females

Comments

1. In line with national research, males are more likely to have committed crime and more likely to have been a victim of crime than females, except in the case of domestic violence where both sexes have similar victim rates.

2. Students from natural parent families are the lowest risk family group for crime while those living in other* family arrangements are the highest risk.

3. Current cannabis use is associated with repeated arrests with users almost ten times more likely (7.7%) to have been arrested many times than non users (0.7%).

4. Four times more males (8.3%) than females (2.0%) have taken a weapon to college. Students who have carried a weapon to college are twice as likely (69.1%) to regularly watch films, games and videos that include explicit violence than those who have not (33.5%).

5. More than one in ten males who drive have driven at least once under the influence of alcohol over the past year. Nearly a quarter of males and 6.1% of females who drive have driven under the influence of illegal drugs over the past year.

* Other family arrangement includes living with relatives/guardian, in a care home, in foster care.

[1] http://www.statistics.gov.uk/cci/nugget. asp?id=467

Sexual behaviour

This section presents information on the sexual behaviour of students in West Sussex colleges of Further and Higher Education. Comparative information is provided, where possible, from the National Survey of Sexual Lifestyle and Attitudes that interviewed over 11 thousand people aged 16 to 44 years.[1]

The House of Commons Health Select Committee recently described a national crisis in sexual health. Alarmed by dramatic increases in the rates of sexually transmitted infections (STIs) and concerned by over-stretched, under-resourced genitourinary (GU) medicine services, the Committee has called for urgent action.[2] There is an epidemic of sexually transmitted infections, with numbers of the common STIs having doubled in the last decade or so. There is particular concern about the increasing rate of Chlamydia in young people as it can cause future infertility. An opportunistic national screening programme for Chlamydia among the under 25s has been introduced.

It is important to remember that the majority of responding students are single (estimated to be around 96%), with only a small proportion married (around 1%) and a few who are divorced or separated. A large proportion of students (87%) are living with their parents, 2.8% live on their own, 2.8% with partners and 2.2% live in university accommodation. The other 5% live with friends or have other* living arrangements. (See Section 2 on demography).

Sexual activity

Table 11.1 shows the proportion of students who have had sexual intercourse by age and sex. Just under three-quarters of students have had sexual intercourse. For all age groups, except the 20 and over group, more females than males have been sexually active and, as expected, a higher proportion of older students have had sexual intercourse.

Age of first sexual intercourse

The median age of first sexual intercourse was 15 years for males and 16 years for females. The National Survey of Sexual Attitudes and Lifestyles 2001 reported the median age of first intercourse in the 16-19 age group was 16 years for both males and females.[3]

First sex before age 16

The 1993 survey of sexual behaviour reported that 18.7% of females and 27.6% males in the 16-19 age group had first sex before the age of 16. The 2001 national survey reported the figures as 25.6% for females and 29.9% for males.[4]

Table 11.1 Have had sexual intercourse by age for all students						
	Males		Females		All	
	N	(%)	N	(%)	N	(%)
16 years	132	(58.4)	110	(62.5)	242	(60.2)
17 years	381	(67.2)	339	(72.6)	721	(69.8)
18 years	263	(77.8)	166	(77.8)	430	(78.9)
19 years	113	(79.6)	75	(85.2)	188	(81.7)
20 years	172	(86.9)	74	(83.1)	246	(85.7)

Table 11.2 Proportion who first had sex before the age of 16, by age at time of survey		
Age at survey	Males	Females
	Percentage who had first sex before age 16	
17 years	59.8	51.9
18 years	46.9	37.8
19 years	42.3	35.2
20 and over	40.0	18.8

Table 11.2 shows the proportion of students who had first sex before the age of 16 at the time of the survey.

The findings suggest that the proportion of West Sussex FE and HE students having first sex before the age of 16 is higher than reported in the national survey.

Family structure

Figure 11.1 shows the proportion of single students who have had sexual intercourse by family structure. Highest rates on sexual activity were found among students living in stepparent families (81.6%) and lowest rates among students living with their natural parents (65.8%).

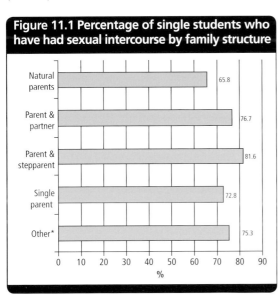

Figure 11.1 Percentage of single students who have had sexual intercourse by family structure

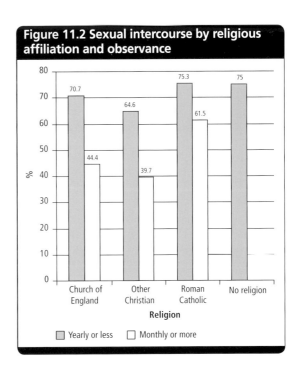

Figure 11.2 Sexual intercourse by religious affiliation and observance

Religion

Religious affiliation and observance has an established association with sexual behaviour. Figure 11.2 shows the percentage of single students who have had sexual intercourse by religious observance. Students who attend meetings or services monthly or more often are less likely to have had sexual intercourse than those who attend less often. For example, among students affiliated to the Church of England, of those who attend at least monthly 44.4% have had sexual intercourse compared with 70.7% of infrequent attendees. Lowest rates of sexual intercourse among single students were reported among the Other Christian group who attend services at least monthly (39.7%).

Table 11.3 Had sexual intercourse by smoking experience for single students				
	%			
	Never	**Used to**	**Occasional**	**Regular**
Smoking	54.9	82.1	77.7	92.3
Cannabis	56.6	89.1	85.6	94.0

Smoking, alcohol and cannabis

The survey showed a strong relationship between a number of lifestyle factors and the likelihood of students having had sexual intercourse. For example, single students who smoke cigarettes regularly (92.3%) are almost twice as likely to have had sexual intercourse as those who have never smoked (54.9%).

A similar trend is observed for alcohol experience. Of students who do not smoke, 77.4% who drink alcohol regularly have been sexually active compared with 35.9% of those who have never drunk alcohol.

Students were asked whether they were under the influence of alcohol when they first had sex; 29.9% of males and 19.1% of females said they were. There was an age gradient with just over a third of males and quarter of females who first had sex aged under 16 being under the influence of alcohol.

Should have waited longer

Students were asked:

Looking back to the first time you had sexual intercourse do you think you should have waited longer?

Over a third of females (36.9%) and just under a fifth of males (19.0%) thought that they should have waited longer before having first sex. The national survey reported that 41.8% of females and 20.4% males wished they had waited longer. Figure 11.3 shows that among females who had

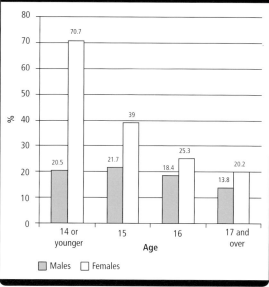

Figure 11.3 Percentage who thought they should have waited longer before first intercourse by age at first sexual intercourse

first intercourse at age 14 or younger, 70.7% thought that they should have waited longer, compared with just 20.5% of males in the same age group.

Being under the influence of alcohol at the time of first sexual intercourse is closely associated with whether female students felt they should have waited longer. Of females under the influence of alcohol, 69.2% thought they should have waited longer compared with 31.3% who were not under the influence. Among males there was almost no difference between those under the influence and those not under the influence of alcohol (19.9% compared with 18.7%).

Table 11.4 Percentage who said they should have waited longer by whether they were under the influence of alcohol at time of first sexual intercourse

Age at first sex	Males		Females	
	Alcohol Yes	Alcohol No	Alcohol Yes	Alcohol No
14 years & younger	15.4	23.5	73.7	69.5
15 years	19.2	23.1	56.3	33.6
16 years	28.4	15.1	47.5	20.8
17 years & older	17.4	12.7	69.2	14.7
All ages	19.9	18.7	69.2	31.3

There is also an age gradient among females who were under the influence of alcohol at first sexual intercourse and reported they should have waited longer, with the largest difference among those who became sexually active at age 17 or older (69.2% compared with 14.7%) (Table 11.4).

Contraception use at first intercourse

Students were asked whether they used contraception when they first had sexual intercourse. The national survey showed that in the 16-19 age group, 7.4% of males and 9.8% of females did not use contraception at the time of their first sexual intercourse. This survey showed that 21.5% of males and 11.0% of females in the same age group did not use contraception on the first occasion.

Those who were 14 or under at first intercourse were the least likely to use contraception. The national survey suggests that this may be caused by those at a younger age being lacking in confidence, due to their age, to seek contraceptive advice or supplies, and also the sporadic nature of sexual activity in this age group[5].

Figure 11.4 shows the proportion of students who did not use contraception by age of first intercourse.

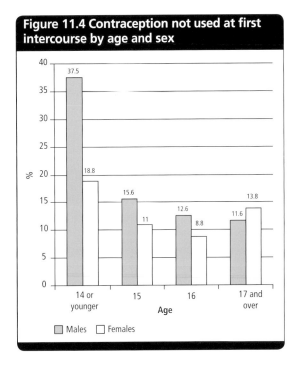

Figure 11.4 Contraception not used at first intercourse by age and sex

Among both males (37.5%) and females (18.8%) those who had their first intercourse aged 14 years or younger were the least likely to use contraception. The national survey found that 17.9% of males and 21.7% of females in the same age group did not use contraception. Among female students who reported first intercourse at age 17 or over, 13.8% reported not using contraception compared with 11.0% of those who reported first intercourse at age 15.

Being under the influence of alcohol at the time of first sexual intercourse, as expected, had an impact on the use of contraception, as shown in Table 11.5. Females as a group were twice as likely not to use contraception if they were under the influence of alcohol than if not (20.0% compared with 10.3%).

The method of contraceptive used at first intercourse was virtually identical between males and females: 89.6% used a condom, 7.4% the pill, 1.2% withdrawal and 1.7% used other methods.

Sexual orientation

Table 11.6 describes the sexual orientation of the survey population.

Number of sexual partners

The median number of sexual partners was three among males and two among females. Over a third (36.4%) of male students and nearly a quarter (24.6%) of female students have had five or more sexual partners.

Sexually transmitted infections (STIs)

Among males, 19.9% have had a test for a STI and 6.1% have had an STI. The figures for females are 27.8% and 2.9% respectively. Figure 11.5 shows the relationship between the number of sexual partners and having had an STI. Among those who have had three or more sexual partners, males are nine times and females three times more likely to have had a STI compared with those who have had one or two partners.

Table 11.5 Percentage who did not use contraception at time of first sexual intercourse by whether under the influence of alcohol

	Male		Female	
	(%)Under influence of alcohol at first sex			
	Yes	No	Yes	No
14 or younger	46.2	32.6	21.1	17.9
15	19.2	12.9	22.9	7.2
16	20.0	10.0	17.1	7.0
17 or over	19.6	8.2	23.1	12.8
All ages	29.8	17.0	20.0	10.3

Table 11.6 Sexual orientation by gender

Sexual orientation	Male		Female	
	N	(%)	N	(%)
Heterosexual	1039	(95.0)	728	(92.6)
Bisexual	15	(1.4)	41	(5.2)
Lesbian	-	-	4	(0.5)
Gay	20	(1.8)	-	-
Transsexual	8	(0.7)	-	-
Unsure	12	(1.1)	13	(1.7)
Total	1094	(100.0)	786	(100.0)

Table 11.7 Pregnancy rate of single students aged under 19 by use of contraception at first intercourse			
	Used contraception	Did not use contraception	All
	(%)		
Males	7.7	26.2	11.4
Females	7.0	29.8	9.5

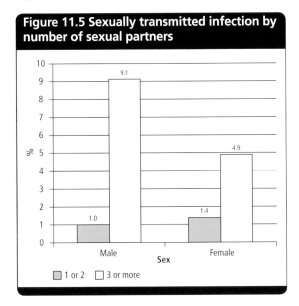

Figure 11.5 Sexually transmitted infection by number of sexual partners

☐ 1 or 2   ☐ 3 or more

Pregnancy

In response to the question; Have you ever been pregnant or got someone pregnant? 13.9% of males and 10.5% of female students responded that they had.

Contraception and pregnancy

The national survey of sexual behaviour states that 'the risks of unplanned pregnancy amongst the young make the question of contraception at first intercourse an important focus in the context of sexual health'.[6] The use of contraception at first intercourse is seen as a proxy for knowledge of, and access to, contraception. Among single students, 83.0% reported using contraception at first sexual intercourse (79.5% of males and 87.9% of females).

Table 11.7 shows the relationship between any pregnancy and contraceptive use at first intercourse for single students.

Of male students aged under 19, who used contraception at first intercourse, 7.7% had since got someone pregnant, compared with 26.2% of those who did not use contraception at first intercourse.

Of female students aged 19 and over, who used contraception at first intercourse, 7.0% had since become pregnant, compared with 29.8% of those who did not use contraceptives at first intercourse.

First sex before age 16

The national survey of sexual behaviour shows that first sexual intercourse is an indicator for other risk behaviour.

Table 11.8 Age at first sex: percentage with risk factor		
	15 and younger	16 or over
	(%)	
STI test	31.0	16.9
ST infection	5.9	3.1
3 or more sexual partners	72.2	37.6
Pregnancy	20.0	5.5

Comments

1. The proportion of West Sussex FE and HE students in the 16-19 age group who had first sex before the age of 16 was higher than that reported in the 2001 national survey of sexual lifestyles. In this survey, 37.8% of 18-year-old females had first sex before 16, 35.2% of 19-year-olds (see Table 11.2) compared with 25.6% of 16 to 19-year-olds in the national survey. There is a similar picture among males. In this survey, 42.3% of 19-year-olds were sexual active by age 16 compared with 29.9% of 16 to 19-year-olds in the national survey. This finding suggests that young people are becoming sexually active at an earlier age.

2. Almost one in four females thought that they should have waited longer before having sexual intercourse for the first time.

3. Almost nine out of ten female students used contraception at first intercourse, compared with eight out of ten males. Among single females aged under 19 who used contraception at first intercourse, 7.4% had become pregnant. Among those aged over 19, 12.0% of students who used contraception at first intercourse had been pregnant at some point.

4. There is an association between the number of sexual partners and the likelihood of acquiring a sexually transmitted infection.

* Other family arrangement includes living with relatives/guardian, in a care home, or in foster care.

[1] Sexual Attitudes and Lifestyles, Johnson et al., Blackwell Scientific Publications 1994

[2] The crisis in sexual health and developing genitourinary medicine services: lessons from a primary care trust. Authors: Laverty, Susan1; Pugh, R Nicholas1; Joseph, A.T.2 Source: International Journal of STD & AIDS, Volume 17, Number 1, January 2006 , pp. 37-43(7)

[3] Kaye Wellings et al. Sexual behaviour in Britain: early heterosexual experience, The Lancet, December 2001, 358, 9296, page 1843

[4] Kaye Wellings et al. Sexual behaviour in Britain: early heterosexual experience, The Lancet, December 2001, 358, 9296, page 1844

[5] Sexual Attitudes and Lifestyles, Johnson et al., Blackwell Scientific Publications 1994, page 87

[6] Sexual Attitudes and Lifestyles, Johnson et al., Blackwell Scientific Publications 1994, page 86

Leisure time

What a young person does with their leisure time depends on three things: their own interests and imagination, the kind of leisure facilities available and, of course, money. A common complaint among young people is that there is nothing for them to do, and finding something interesting to do is not always easy. Yet sometimes the most difficult thing for young people is to get motivated enough to do something.

This section deals with students' leisure time activities. Questions were asked about TV viewing, Internet use, newspaper readership and cultural activities.

TV viewing

Table 12.1 shows the response to the question, On an average day, how much time do you spend watching TV? The median amount of time spent watching TV is 120 minutes for both males and females. Just over a quarter of students watch TV for more than three hours a day.

Computer games

There is a large difference between males and females in the amount of time spent playing computer games. Three-quarters of female students (75.3%) do not play computer games, compared with a quarter of males (24.4%). Two out of five males (40.6%) spend over an hour a day on computer games.

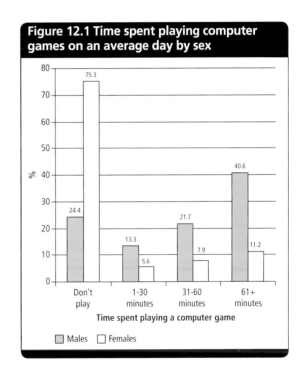

Figure 12.1 Time spent playing computer games on an average day by sex

Table 12.1 Time spent watching TV				
	Males		**Females**	
	N	**(%)**	**N**	**(%)**
0	44	(3.0)	29	(2.7)
1-60 minutes	348	(23.6)	241	(22.7)
61-120 minutes	395	(26.8)	327	(30.8)
121-180 minutes	303	(20.6)	224	(21.1)
181+ minutes	384	(26.1)	242	(22.8)
Total	1474	(100)	1063	(100)

Access to the Internet

Overall, males tend to use the Internet more than females; the median time for males is 120 minutes compared to 90 minutes for females.

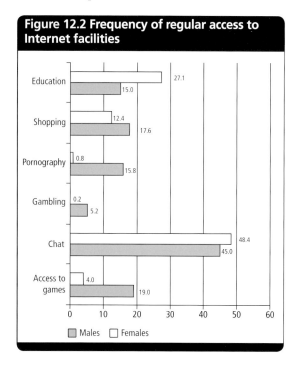

Figure 12.2 Frequency of regular access to Internet facilities

The Internet is not used by 13% of students; a third of students use the Internet for an hour per day; about 20% use it for more than 3 hours per day. Figure 12.2 shows the frequency of regular access to various Internet facilities. Internet chatting was the most common facility used regularly by both males (45.0%) and females (48.4%). There is a large sex differential in access to pornography and in access to computer games and gambling, with males having much higher rates. Females are more likely to use the internet for educational purposes.

Internet by age

There were a few interesting differences by age. Regular access to Internet chat rooms was more common among female students aged 18 and under (52.7%) than those aged over 19 (28.9%). A similar pattern was observed among male

students (48.0% v 35.2%). Regular access to online education also showed a variation by age with older students of both sexes more likely to access education. Regular access to pornography was most common by the youngest students, with 18.0% of 16-year-olds regularly viewing pornography compared with 11.6% of students aged 20 and over.

Newspapers

Over a quarter of students (27.9%) do not regularly read a newspaper. By far the most frequently read newspaper is The Sun (39.2%), followed by The Mail (8.4%). The most frequently read broadsheet is The Times (3.5%), followed by The Guardian, (1.8%), The Daily Telegraph (1.4%) and The Independent (1.4%).

Adult only films

In response to the question about viewing adult only films and videos, and viewing films, videos or games that include explicit violence, there was a large difference between males and females, as shown in Tables 12.2 and 12.3. Males (16.6%) are eight times more likely to regularly view sexually explicit videos than females (1.9%).

Table 12.2 Viewing sexually explicit films or videos

	(%)	
	Males	Females
Never	39.1	85.4
Occasionally	44.3	12.7
Regularly	16.6	1.9
Total	100.0	100.0

Table 12.3 Viewing explicitly violent films or videos		
	(%)	
	Males	**Females**
Never	3.7	20.8
Occasionally	46.2	64.3
Regularly	50.1	14.8
Total	100.0	100.0

A similar picture emerges with regard to violent films, with males being three times more likely to view them regularly (50.1%) than females (14.8%).

Sport, culture, volunteering

Interesting differences by sex were seen in the responses given to questions on sport, culture and volunteering. In the past 12 months, more male students (59.7%) than females (44.8%) regularly participated in organised sporting activities such as football, rugby, hockey, netball and exercise classes. In the past 12 months, more female students (62.4%) visited an art gallery, museum, theatre or heritage site than males (39.9%). Volunteering was more popular among females: in the past 12 months almost a third of female students (32.1%) undertook formal volunteering (on average two or more hours of unpaid work per week) compared with 17.4% of male students.

Comments

1. Young adults spend a lot of their leisure time watching TV, accessing the Internet and playing computer games. Males tend to spend more time on the Internet and playing computer games than females.

2. Access to pornography and sexually explicit films/videos is almost exclusively a male activity. A small proportion of males regularly access pornography on the Internet.

3. While males spend more time on organised sport, females are more likely to be involved with cultural activities, such as visiting an art gallery or museum and to be engaged in formal volunteering.

Views and opinions

This section deals with the views and opinions of young people on topical political, moral and cultural issues. The purpose is to gain some idea of how student's view the wider world.

Voting in the 2005 General Election

Most students aged 19 and over at the time of the survey (2007) were old enough to vote in the 2005 election. Table 13.1 shows voting patterns among students aged over 19. Among both males (43.3%) and females (40.8%) the largest group are those who did not want to vote, almost 10% of students were not on the electoral register and a further 10% were not aware of the election. This suggests that almost two-thirds of students who were eligible to vote did not do so.

Table 13.1 Students aged 19 and over at time of survey and old enough to vote and voting at the 2005 election	(%)	
	Male	Female
Yes, I voted	39.6	33.8
No, not on register	8.2	12.7
No, not aware of election	8.9	12.7
No, did not want to vote	43.3	40.8
Total	100.0	100.0

Topical political issues

Students were presented with a number of statements on topical issues and asked whether they agreed or disagreed.

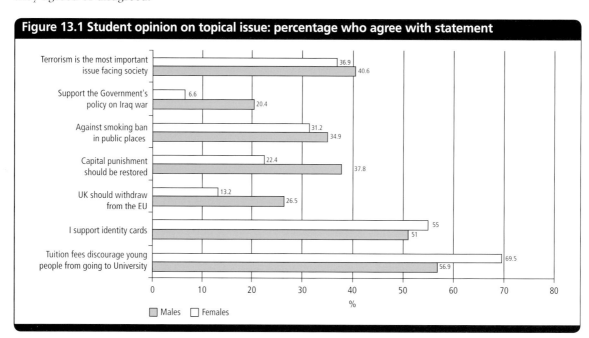

Figure 13.1 Student opinion on topical issue: percentage who agree with statement

- Terrorism is the most important issue facing society — Males 36.9, Females 40.6
- Support the Government's policy on Iraq war — Males 6.6, Females 20.4
- Against smoking ban in public places — Males 31.2, Females 34.9
- Capital punishment should be restored — Males 22.4, Females 37.8
- UK should withdraw from the EU — Males 13.2, Females 26.5
- I support identity cards — Males 55, Females 51
- Tuition fees discourage young people from going to University — Males 69.5, Females 56.9

Males Females

%

Just over half of the survey population support the concept of identity cards. Male students (26.5%) were twice as likely as female students (13.2%) to think that the UK should withdraw from the EU. There is a similar sex differential in the issue of capital punishment with 37.8% of males in favour of restoring capital punishment compared with 22.4% of females (Figure 13.1).

The question *Are you interested in issues concerning your local council/area?* produced a positive response in 34.1% of males and 38.7% of females. Around two-thirds of students (62.9%) feel that parents in their area do not take enough responsibility for the behaviour of their children. In response to the question *Do you feel people in your local area live in harmony together?* only 40% of students responded in the affirmative.

Opinions about moral issues

Students were asked to express an opinion on a number of moral questions. Table 13.2 shows the proportion of students who believe that a particular behaviour is morally wrong.

An affair between married people was the behaviour that received the greatest moral censure, while sex between unmarried people was felt to be morally wrong by about 1 in 20 students. Females tended to be more against smoking cannabis (34.4%) and drinking alcohol excessively (32.9%) and males were more against overeating (28.0%).

Moral issues by religion

Issues around sexual behaviour show interesting differences when analysed by religious affiliation and religious observance.

Figure 13.2 and Figure 13.3 show students' response to questions on sex between unmarried adults and on abortion by religious observance. For each religion those who attend meetings or services more frequently are more likely to believe that sex outside marriage and abortion is wrong. The group that is most likely to believe that sex between unmarried adults in wrong is Other Christians (57.4%) who attended weekly. They are also the group most likely to believe that abortion is wrong (68.1%).

Table13.2 Percentage of students who believe behaviour is morally wrong		
	%	
	Male	Female
Smoking cannabis	24.3	34.4
Drinking alcohol excessively	27.1	32.9
Sex between unmarried adults	6.7	5.5
Gambling	13.0	21.4
Overeating	28.0	19.2
Having an abortion	17.7	21.7
Married people having an affair	60.6	72.1

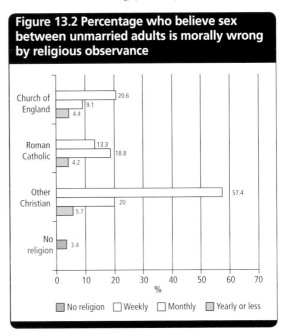

Figure 13.2 Percentage who believe sex between unmarried adults is morally wrong by religious observance

Table 13.3 Percentage who believe married people having an affair is morally wrong by religious observance

	Yearly or less	Monthly	Weekly
Church of England	68.5	63.6	58.8
Other Christian	70.8	80.0	80.9
Roman Catholic	74.7	68.8	80.0
No religion	63.8	-	-

Figure 13.3 Percentage who believe abortion is morally wrong by religious observance

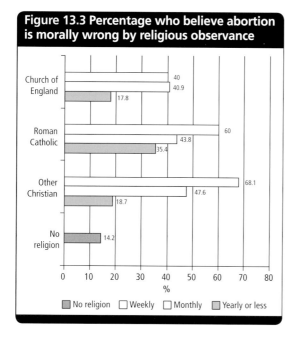

Figure 13.4 Agree that it is morally wrong to use cannabis by cannabis experience

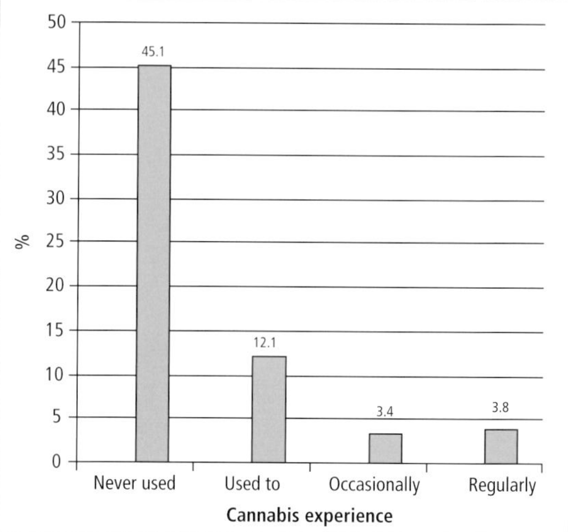

The response to the question about married people having an affair is shown in Table 13.3. Over two-thirds (67.9%) of students believe that affairs are wrong, with Roman Catholics and Other Christians who attend services weekly being the most opposed.

Cannabis users have different views on a number of the moral issues. Figure 13.4 shows the proportion of those who believe that it is morally wrong to smoke cannabis, by cannabis experience.

As expected, there is a clear gradient: those who have used cannabis are less likely than those who have never used cannabis to believe it is morally wrong. This also applies to believing that sex between unmarried people is wrong (3.0% and 8.6% respectively) and less likely to believe that abortion is morally wrong (14.9% and 22.7% respectively).

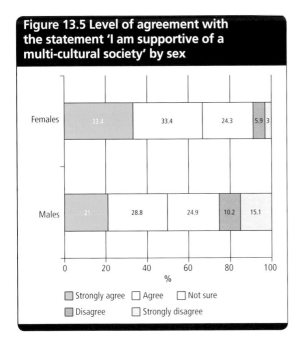

Figure 13.5 Level of agreement with the statement 'I am supportive of a multi-cultural society' by sex

Females: 33.4 | 33.4 | 24.3 | 5.9 | 3
Males: 21 | 28.8 | 24.9 | 10.2 | 15.1

☐ Strongly agree ☐ Agree ☐ Not sure
☐ Disagree ☐ Strongly disagree

Multi-cultural society

Students were asked whether they agreed or disagreed with the statement:

I am supportive of a multi-cultural society.

As shown in Figure 13.5, half of male students (49.8%) and two-thirds of female students (66.8%) agree with the statement. A quarter of both males and females were not sure whether they agreed or disagreed.

Comments

1. It is disappointing that around two out of five students did not want to vote in the last general election. Almost one in five students had not registered to vote or were unaware that there was an election. These finding suggest a lethargy around political issues. Only one in three students expressed an interest in issues concerning their local council.

2. Just under two-thirds of students thought that tuition fees discouraged young people from going to University. The political policy that gained least support from students was the Iraq war, with only 6.6% of females agreeing with the policy.

3. The issue that received the greatest moral censure was an affair between married people: two out of three students believed that it is wrong.

4. Sex between unmarried people was believed to be morally acceptable by 19 out of 20 students. Moral issues showed interesting differences by religion and religious observance.

	Sex		Age				Family structure (of those living with parents)					Religion				Health Status		
	Male	Female	16	17	18	19+	M&F	P&P	Step	Single	Other	CoE	Oth Chr	RC	None	Good	Fairly good	Not good
Smoking																		
Never	46.5	49.5	50.0	48.5	46.5	46.1	53.6	38.9	37.2	43.8	37.7	52.5	64.0	48.3	43.1	57.8	37.5	26.9
Stopped	10.9	11.1	10.2	10.2	9.9	14.0	10.0	13.9	13.3	9.6	16.4	10.2	9.9	9.8	11.2	9.9	12.6	10.5
Occasional	13.0	15.0	12.9	14.9	13.3	13.3	13.6	23.1	8.5	15.6	11.5	13.6	9.9	16.1	14.3	13.6	14.5	10.5
Regular	29.6	24.4	26.9	26.4	30.4	26.6	22.8	24.1	41.0	31.0	34.4	23.7	16.3	25.9	31.4	18.7	35.5	52.0
Total	100.0	100.0	100.0	100.0	100.0	100.0	100.0	100.0	100.0	100.0	100.0	100.0	100.0	100.0	100.0	100.0	100.0	100.0
Alcohol																		
Never/rarely	17.1	17.9	22.3	17.6	12.0	18.6	18.1	9.3	15.5	18.5	14.9	17.1	22.5	12.4	14.7	19.3	15.8	12.9
Occasional	47.2	59.4	53.7	54.4	51.5	48.3	52.6	57.0	52.9	52.7	51.2	55.2	60.3	62.8	50.5	53.7	52.3	40.0
Regular	35.7	22.7	24.0	28.0	36.5	33.0	29.3	33.6	31.6	28.8	33.9	27.7	17.2	24.8	34.8	27.0	31.9	47.1
Total	100.0	100.0	100.0	100.0	100.0	100.0	100.0	100.0	100.0	100.0	100.0	100.0	100.0	100.0	100.0	100.0	100.0	100.0
Binge Drinking																		
Never/rarely	25.2	29.5	28.5	26.6	25.0	28.2	27.6	24.3	23.2	25.7	24.6	28.6	37.4	25.9	22.9	30.6	23.6	16.5
Occasional	44.9	51.7	48.1	47.3	45.4	51.1	48.`	47.6	48.0	48.5	44.7	49.9	48.1	54.7	48.2	46.3	50.8	42.4
Regular	29.8	18.8	23.4	26.1	29.6	20.7	24.3	28.2	28.8	25.7	30.7	21.5	14.4	19.4	28.9	23.1	25.6	41.1
Total	100.0	100.0	100.0	100.0	100.0	100.0	100.0	100.0	100.0	100.0	100.0	100.0	100.0	100.0	100.0	100.0	100.0	100.0
Cannabis																		
Never	50.8	66.7	65.7	60.3	52.9	50.2	63.5	48.1	50.6	53.3	47.9	63.9	70.6	60.0	52.0	63.0	53.6	32.3
Stopped	20.9	17.3	16.5	16.7	21.1	25.5	16.0	25.0	25.6	21.2	21.5	19.7	12.4	15.7	20.9	17.9	20.0	25.7
Occasional	17.4	13.6	10.9	16.6	18.2	15.7	14.3	20.2	13.9	16.4	19.0	12.0	12.9	17.9	18.1	13.7	18.3	21.0
Regular	10.9	2.5	6.8	6.4	7.8	8.7	6.2	6.7	10.0	9.0	11.6	4.3	4.0	6.4	8.9	5.5	8.1	21.0
Total	100.0	100.0	100.0	100.0	100.0	100.0	100.0	100.0	100.0	100.0	100.0	100.0	100.0	100.0	100.0	100.0	100.0	100.0
Portions of fruit & veg a day																		
0-2	53.5	42.2	45.4	47.3	52.3	50.5	47.1	46.7	52.2	51.2	48.7	42.6	45.9	52.5	52.0	43.6	54.0	60.6
3-4	36.4	42.6	41.7	39.1	36.8	39.1	39.9	45.8	34.6	39.0	34.5	43.6	40.3	34.5	37.4	41.6	37.1	27.6
5 or more	10.1	15.2	12.9	13.6	11.0	10.4	13.0	7.5	13.2	9.8	16.8	13.8	13.8	12.9	10.7	14.8	8.9	11.8
Total	100.0	100.0	100.0	100.0	100.0	100.0	100.0	100.0	100.0	100.0	100.0	100.0	100.0	100.0	100.0	100.0	100.0	100.0

	Sex		Age				Family structure (of those living with parents)					Religion				Health Status		
	Male	Female	16	17	18	19+	M&F	P&P	Step	Single	Other	CoE	Oth Chr	RC	None	Good	Fairly good	Not good
Weight perception																		
Underweight	11.1	5.3	6.7	8.3	8.2	11.2	8.8	10.4	9.9	9.1	4.9	7.5	8.4	6.9	9.5	7.1	8.7	20.8
Normal	66.8	62.8	66.6	67.5	64.0	61.6	67.0	63.2	72.5	60.8	59.3	65.4	65.3	66.7	66.1	72.6	58.9	38.7
Slightly overweight	15.7	23.8	18.3	17.7	21.3	19.1	18.8	18.9	12.6	20.5	20.3	19.4	19.8	21.5	18.5	15.9	23.6	19.6
Moderately overweight	4.8	5.9	5.8	5.3	4.7	5.7	4.5	6.6	2.7	7.3	6.5	6.0	5.4	4.2	4.6	3.5	6.4	12.5
Very overweight	1.5	2.2	2.6	1.1	1.8	2.5	1.0	0.9	2.2	2.2	8.9	1.7	.0	0.7	1.3	0.8	2.4	8.3
Total	100.0	100.0	100.0	100.0	100.0	100.0	100.0	100.0	100.0	100.0	100.0	100.0	100.0	100.0	100.0	100.0	100.0	100.0
Physical Activity																		
None	15.9	21.6	16.9	16.7	16.6	24.5	16.0	17.0	15.8	18.9	31.9	14.8	15.8	16.8	20.3	16.0	19.5	31.8
1 day	17.5	21.8	18.5	17.8	21.6	19.8	19.5	19.8	18.6	17.2	14.7	21.6	24.6	17.5	17.3	17.9	21.7	17.1
2 days	15.8	18.9	20.0	16.5	18.9	14.4	18.1	21.7	16.9	16.4	16.4	14.3	22.7	19.6	18.0	17.3	16.7	17.1
3 days	20.4	17.7	17.8	21.6	17.9	17.2	19.2	22.6	20.2	20.6	17.2	20.8	13.3	18.9	20.0	20.5	19.0	10.0
4 days	12.6	9.4	12.1	11.3	10.4	11.8	12.2	5.7	10.9	11.8	6.9	13.1	12.3	9.1	10.4	12.2	10.1	9.4
5 days+	17.7	10.6	14.7	16.1	14.6	12.3	15.0	13.2	17.5	15.1	12.9	15.4	11.3	18.2	13.9	16.0	13.0	14.7
Total	100.0	100.0	100.0	100.0	100.0	100.0	100.0	100.0	100.0	100.0	100.0	100.0	100.0	100.0	100.0	100.0	100.0	100.0
Sexually explicit films/videos																		
Never/rarely	39.1	85.4	63.9	63.4	55.4	48.8	61.8	53.8	59.3	56.9	48.8	62.3	70.6	58.3	55.8	59.5	59.7	43.5
Occasional	44.3	12.7	26.2	27.0	33.2	39.6	29.3	36.8	30.2	31.2	31.4	28.5	24.9	32.6	34.3	31.4	30.3	31.8
Regular	16.6	1.9	9.9	9.5	11.4	11.6	8.9	9.4	10.4	11.9	19.8	9.2	4.5	9.0	9.9	9.1	10.1	24.7
Total	100.0	100.0	100.0	100.0	100.0	100.0	100.0	100.0	100.0	100.0	100.0	100.0	100.0	100.0	100.0	100.0	100.0	100.0
Explicitly violent films/videos																		
Never/rarely	3.7	20.8	12.0	10.8	9.8	11.3	11.0	4.7	9.7	11.7	7.4	12.8	21.5	11.1	8.9	12.0	9.2	9.3
Occasional	46.2	64.3	54.5	53.4	54.4	53.7	55.4	63.2	50.8	47.9	51.6	59.5	54.6	52.8	52.1	54.8	54.0	43.0
Regular	50.1	14.8	33.5	35.9	35.8	35.0	33.6	32.1	39.5	40.4	41.0	27.7	23.9	36.1	39.0	33.2	36.7	47.7
Total	100.0	100.0	100.0	100.0	100.0	100.0	100.0	100.0	100.0	100.0	100.0	100.0	100.0	100.0	100.0	100.0	100.0	100.0

	Sex		Age				Family structure (of those living with parents)					Religion				Health Status		
	Male	Female	16	17	18	19+	M&F	P&P	Step	Single	Other	CoE	Oth Chr	RC	None	Good	Fairly good	Not good
Organised sporting activities																		
Yes	59.7	44.8	57.8	55.6	51.7	47.7	56.0	54.2	56.5	49.8	52.1	58.2	49.8	55.6	51.0	58.2	48.3	43.5
No	40.3	55.2	42.2	44.4	48.3	52.3	44.0	45.8	43.5	50.2	47.9	41.8	50.2	44.4	49.0	41.8	51.7	56.5
Total	100.0	100.0	100.0	100.0	100.0	100.0	100.0	100.0	100.0	100.0	100.0	100.0	100.0	100.0	100.0	100.0	100.0	100.0
Formal volunteering																		
Yes	17.4	32.1	26.2	24.4	25.3	19.5	24.7	15.9	23.8	21.9	23.5	28.3	33.3	19.9	20.1	23.3	24.1	22.7
No	82.6	67.9	73.8	75.6	74.7	80.5	75.3	84.1	76.2	78.1	76.5	71.7	66.7	80.1	79.9	76.7	75.9	77.3
Total	100.0	100.0	100.0	100.0	100.0	100.0	100.0	100.0	100.0	100.0	100.0	100.0	100.0	100.0	100.0	100.0	100.0	100.0
Mood: depressed																		
Never/rarely	53.8	36.4	46.4	47.9	44.7	45.7	50.2	50.5	48.1	40.9	41.2	47.2	45.1	41.3	48.3	55.7	36.7	24.9
Occasional	39.8	50.4	43.6	43.6	45.4	44.9	42.1	39.3	43.2	49.2	41.2	44.0	46.1	49.0	43.2	39.2	50.8	48.5
Regular	6.4	13.2	10.0	8.5	10.0	9.4	7.8	10.3	8.7	10.0	17.6	8.8	8.8	9.8	8.5	5.1	12.6	26.6
Total	100.0	100.0	100.0	100.0	100.0	100.0	100.0	100.0	100.0	100.0	100.0	100.0	100.0	100.0	100.0	100.0	100.0	100.0
Stress																		
Never/rarely	44.7	24.7	38.1	36.3	36.1	35.5	39.0	40.2	37.0	32.9	26.7	36.6	38.0	31.3	37.0	45.3	26.7	17.2
Occasional	44.1	51.1	44.8	47.6	45.6	49.1	46.3	41.1	44.0	49.1	50.0	47.3	45.9	47.9	46.8	44.6	51.3	40.8
Regular	11.2	24.1	17.1	16.1	18.3	15.4	14.7	18.7	19.0	18.0	23.3	16.1	16.1	20.8	16.2	10.1	22.1	42.0
Total	100.0	100.0	100.0	100.0	100.0	100.0	100.0	100.0	100.0	100.0	100.0	100.0	100.0	100.0	100.0	100.0	100.0	100.0
Enough sleep																		
Yes	47.4	40.5	43.5	45.5	42.2	45.3	47.4	41.1	42.5	38.6	44.2	45.5	45.9	45.5	43.0	53.7	36.3	18.6
No	52.6	59.5	56.5	54.5	57.8	54.7	52.6	58.9	57.5	61.4	55.8	54.5	54.1	54.5	57.0	46.3	63.7	81.4
Total	100.0	100.0	100.0	100.0	100.0	100.0	100.0	100.0	100.0	100.0	100.0	100.0	100.0	100.0	100.0	100.0	100.0	100.0
Self-harmed																		
Yes	6.4	12.9	11.1	11.1	7.6	5.5	8.1	10.4	10.8	8.8	16.7	8.4	9.8	9.8	8.0	5.8	11.7	22.8
No	93.6	87.1	88.9	88.9	92.4	94.5	91.9	89.6	89.2	91.2	83.3	91.6	90.2	90.2	92.0	94.2	88.3	77.2
Total	100.0	100.0	100.0	100.0	100.0	100.0	100.0	100.0	100.0	100.0	100.0	100.0	100.0	100.0	100.0	100.0	100.0	100.0

	Sex		Age				Family structure (of those living with parents)					Religion				Health Status		
	Male	Female	16	17	18	19+	M&F	P&P	Step	Single	Other	CoE	Oth Chr	RC	None	Good	Fairly good	Not good
Seriously contemplated suicide																		
Yes	7.0	9.8	9.1	8.6	8.1	6.7	6.6	6.7	6.1	8.3	23.5	5.5	8.9	9.0	8.1	4.5	10.9	24.1
No	93.0	90.2	90.9	91.4	91.9	93.3	93.4	93.3	93.9	91.7	76.5	94.5	91.1	91.0	91.9	95.5	89.1	75.9
Total	100.0	100.0	100.0	100.0	100.0	100.0	100.0	100.0	100.0	100.0	100.0	100.0	100.0	100.0	100.0	100.0	100.0	100.0
Been bullied																		
Yes	10.6	14.5	16.1	13.3	11.7	8.1	10.3	13.1	18.3	11.9	24.6	11.6	16.1	13.8	11.2	9.7	13.7	25.7
No	89.4	85.5	83.9	86.7	88.3	91.9	89.7	86.9	81.7	88.1	75.4	88.4	83.9	86.2	88.8	90.3	86.3	74.3
Total	100.0	100.0	100.0	100.0	100.0	100.0	100.0	100.0	100.0	100.0	100.0	100.0	100.0	100.0	100.0	100.0	100.0	100.0
Been arrested																		
Yes	22.1	4.7	18.2	14.1	15.7	11.9	12.8	15.1	19.6	16.7	24.0	10.8	8.4	10.6	17.1	12.7	15.2	29.2
No	77.9	95.3	81.8	85.9	84.3	88.1	87.2	84.9	80.4	83.3	76.0	89.2	91.6	89.4	82.9	87.3	84.8	70.8
Total	100.0	100.0	100.0	100.0	100.0	100.0	100.0	100.0	100.0	100.0	100.0	100.0	100.0	100.0	100.0	100.0	100.0	100.0
Victim of violent crime																		
Yes	17.8	12.9	16.7	13.6	19.5	15.3	14.0	17.0	19.0	15.9	22.9	16.4	9.9	15.5	15.5	14.1	16.1	15.9
No	82.2	87.1	83.3	86.4	80.5	84.7	86.0	83.0	81.0	84.1	77.1	83.6	90.1	84.5	84.5	85.9	83.9	84.1
Total	100.0	100.0	100.0	100.0	100.0	100.0	100.0	100.0	100.0	100.0	100.0	100.0	100.0	100.0	100.0	100.0	100.0	100.0
Victim of domestic violence																		
Yes	6.1	6.2	7.4	5.2	8.4	4.7	4.4	6.7	8.2	6.9	13.4	4.8	2.5	9.2	6.2	4.2	7.0	18.3
No	93.9	93.8	92.6	94.8	91.6	95.3	95.6	93.3	91.8	93.1	86.6	95.2	97.5	90.8	93.8	95.8	93.0	81.7
Total	100.0	100.0	100.0	100.0	100.0	100.0	100.0	100.0	100.0	100.0	100.0	100.0	100.0	100.0	100.0	100.0	100.0	100.0
Witnessed domestic violence																		
Yes	16.5	12.6	13.5	15.6	17.2	11.4	11.1	15.4	21.7	19.4	27.7	13.1	12.9	17.6	15.0	10.8	18.4	30.8
No	83.5	87.4	86.5	84.4	82.8	88.6	88.9	84.6	78.3	80.6	72.3	86.9	87.1	82.4	85.0	89.2	81.6	69.2
Total	100.0	100.0	100.0	100.0	100.0	100.0	100.0	100.0	100.0	100.0	100.0	100.0	100.0	100.0	100.0	100.0	100.0	100.0
Had sexual intercourse																		
Yes	72.5	74.4	60.2	69.8	78.9	83.8	67.8	78.6	83.0	74.8	77.1	71.0	58.4	75.2	77.0	68.4	78.5	83.2
No	27.5	25.6	39.8	30.2	21.1	16.2	32.2	21.4	17.0	25.2	22.9	29.0	41.6	24.8	23.0	31.6	21.5	16.8
Total	100.0	100.0	100.0	100.0	100.0	100.0	100.0	100.0	100.0	100.0	100.0	100.0	100.0	100.0	100.0	100.0	100.0	100.0

	Sex		Age				Family structure (of those living with parents)					Religion				Health Status		
	Male	Female	16	17	18	19+	M&F	P&P	Step	Single	Other	CoE	Oth Chr	RC	None	Good	Fairly good	Not good
Contraception: first time																		
Yes	77.8	87.7	83.8	82.7	83.1	78.7	84.8	87.5	80.7	82.1	65.2	85.7	81.1	84.5	82.0	83.4	81.6	71.3
No	22.2	12.3	16.2	17.3	16.9	21.3	15.2	12.5	19.3	17.9	34.8	14.3	18.9	15.5	18.0	16.6	18.4	28.7
Total	100.0	100.0	100.0	100.0	100.0	100.0	100.0	100.0	100.0	100.0	100.0	100.0	100.0	100.0	100.0	100.0	100.0	100.0
First time: wished waited																		
Yes	18.8	37.1	26.7	27.5	26.0	24.7	25.2	30.9	23.2	22.7	33.0	28.1	30.3	36.5	23.7	23.3	29.9	27.9
No	81.2	62.9	73.3	72.5	74.0	75.3	74.8	69.1	76.8	77.3	67.0	71.9	69.7	63.5	76.3	76.7	70.1	72.1
Total	100.0	100.0	100.0	100.0	100.0	100.0	100.0	100.0	100.0	100.0	100.0	100.0	100.0	100.0	100.0	100.0	100.0	100.0
Ever had an STI																		
Yes	6.1	2.9	3.3	2.6	7.3	6.0	3.5	6.3	4.5	5.4	4.2	4.0	1.7	6.0	4.1	3.6	5.1	12.5
No	93.9	97.1	96.7	97.4	92.7	94.0	96.5	93.8	95.5	94.6	95.8	96.0	98.3	94.0	95.9	96.4	94.9	87.5
Total	100.0	100.0	100.0	100.0	100.0	100.0	100.0	100.0	100.0	100.0	100.0	100.0	100.0	100.0	100.0	100.0	100.0	100.0

	Sex		Age				Family structure (of those living with parents)					Religion				Health Status		
	Male	Female	16	17	18	19+	M&F	P&P	Step	Single	Other	CoE	Oth Chr	RC	None	Good	Fairly good	Not good
Smoking																		
Never	709	540	210	516	263	250	755	42	70	236	46	374	130	69	551	828	373	46
Stopped	166	121	43	108	56	76	141	15	25	52	20	73	20	14	143	142	125	18
Occasional	198	164	54	159	75	72	191	25	16	84	14	97	20	23	183	195	144	18
Regular	452	266	113	281	172	144	321	26	77	167	42	169	33	37	402	268	353	89
Total	1525	1091	420	1064	566	542	1408	108	188	539	122	713	203	143	1279	1433	995	171
Alcohol																		
Never/rarely	261	197	94	188	68	101	255	10	29	101	18	123	46	18	188	278	157	22
Occasional	720	653	226	582	292	262	742	61	99	287	62	397	123	91	648	774	521	68
Regular	545	249	101	300	207	179	414	36	59	157	41	199	35	36	446	389	318	80
Total	1526	1099	421	1070	567	542	1411	107	187	545	121	719	204	145	1282	1441	996	170
Binge Drinking																		
Never/rarely	364	303	112	266	137	143	366	25	41	133	28	195	70	36	279	415	222	26
Occasional	649	531	189	473	249	259	638	49	85	251	51	341	90	76	586	627	477	67
Regular	431	193	92	261	162	105	323	29	51	133	35	147	27	27	351	313	240	65
Total	1444	1027	393	1000	548	507	1327	103	177	517	114	683	187	139	1216	1355	939	158
Cannabis																		
Never	756	706	270	622	293	266	872	50	91	279	58	447	142	84	646	881	516	54
Stopped	311	183	68	172	117	135	219	26	46	111	26	138	25	22	260	250	193	43
Occasional	259	144	45	171	101	83	197	21	25	86	23	84	25	25	225	191	176	35
Regular	163	26	28	66	43	46	85	7	18	47	14	30	8	9	111	77	78	35
Total	1489	1059	411	1031	554	530	1373	104	180	523	121	699	201	140	1242	1399	963	167
Portions of fruit & veg a day																		
0-2	800	451	187	500	290	262	650	50	95	273	58	300	90	73	654	610	529	103
3-4	545	455	172	413	204	203	551	49	63	208	41	307	79	48	470	581	363	47
5 or more	151	163	53	144	61	54	179	8	24	52	20	97	27	18	134	207	87	20
Total	1496	1069	412	1057	555	519	1380	107	182	533	119	704	196	139	1258	1398	979	170

	Sex		Age				Family structure (of those living with parents)					Religion				Health Status		
	Male	Female	16	17	18	19+	M&F	P&P	Step	Single	Other	CoE	Oth Chr	RC	None	Good	Fairly good	Not good
Weight perception																		
Underweight	167	57	28	88	46	59	122	11	18	49	6	53	17	10	120	101	85	35
Normal	1007	674	277	713	357	325	932	67	132	326	73	461	132	96	834	1030	576	65
Slightly overweight	237	255	76	187	119	101	261	20	23	110	25	137	40	31	233	226	231	33
Moderately overweight	73	63	24	56	26	30	63	7	5	39	8	42	11	6	58	50	63	21
Very overweight	23	24	11	12	10	13	14	1	4	12	11	12	2	1	17	11	23	14
Total	1507	1073	416	1056	558	528	1392	106	182	536	123	705	202	144	1262	1418	978	168
Physical Activity																		
None	240	233	71	175	93	131	223	18	29	101	37	105	32	24	256	227	190	54
1 day	264	235	78	187	121	106	272	21	34	92	17	153	50	25	218	255	212	29
2 days	239	204	84	173	106	77	253	23	31	88	19	101	46	28	227	246	163	29
3 days	308	191	75	227	100	92	268	24	37	110	20	147	27	27	252	292	185	17
4 days	190	101	51	119	58	63	171	6	20	63	8	93	25	13	131	174	99	16
5 days+	267	114	62	169	82	66	209	14	32	81	15	109	23	26	175	227	127	25
Total	1508	1078	421	1050	560	535	1396	106	183	535	116	708	203	143	1259	1421	976	170
Sexually explicit films/videos																		
Never/rarely	580	923	266	666	307	256	656	57	108	301	59	442	142	84	694	836	581	74
Occasional	658	137	109	284	184	208	406	39	55	165	38	202	50	47	426	441	295	54
Regular	247	21	41	100	63	61	123	10	19	63	24	65	9	13	123	128	98	42
Total	1485	1081	416	1050	554	525	1385	106	182	529	121	709	201	144	1243	1405	974	170
Explicitly violent films/videos																		
Never/rarely	56	227	51	115	55	61	155	5	18	64	9	92	44	16	113	172	91	16
Occasional	704	702	231	570	305	290	779	67	94	261	63	426	112	76	665	787	534	74
Regular	763	162	142	383	201	189	472	34	73	220	50	198	49	52	498	476	363	82
Total	1523	1091	424	1068	561	540	1406	106	185	545	122	716	205	144	1276	1435	988	172

	Sex		Age				Family structure (of those living with parents)					Religion				Health Status		
	Male	Female	16	17	18	19+	M&F	P&P	Step	Single	Other	CoE	Oth Chr	RC	None	Good	Fairly good	Not good
Organised sporting activities																		
Yes	908	491	245	595	290	258	790	58	105	271	62	418	102	80	651	837	479	74
No	614	605	179	476	271	283	620	49	81	273	57	300	103	64	625	601	512	96
Total	1522	1096	424	1071	561	541	1410	107	186	544	119	718	205	144	1276	1438	991	170
Formal volunteering																		
Yes	263	350	110	259	142	105	344	17	44	120	28	202	68	28	255	333	237	39
No	1250	740	310	804	419	433	1049	90	141	427	91	512	136	113	1015	1095	746	133
Total	1513	1090	420	1063	561	538	1393	107	185	547	119	714	204	141	1270	1428	983	172
Mood: depressed																		
Never/rarely	817	396	196	508	251	247	705	54	88	221	49	338	92	59	614	798	362	42
Occasional	605	548	184	463	255	243	591	42	79	266	49	315	94	70	550	562	501	82
Regular	97	144	42	90	56	51	109	11	16	54	21	63	18	14	108	73	124	45
Total	1519	1088	422	1061	562	541	1405	107	183	541	119	716	204	143	1272	1433	987	169
Stress																		
Never/rarely	679	271	160	387	203	193	548	43	68	179	32	262	78	45	473	649	265	29
Occasional	669	560	188	507	256	267	651	44	81	267	60	339	94	69	597	639	509	69
Regular	170	264	72	172	103	84	207	20	35	98	28	115	33	30	207	144	219	71
Total	1518	1095	420	1066	562	544	1406	107	184	544	120	716	205	144	1277	1432	993	169
Enough sleep																		
Yes	721	443	185	485	238	245	666	44	79	211	53	325	94	65	549	770	360	32
No	801	651	240	580	326	296	740	63	107	335	67	390	111	78	728	663	632	140
Total	1522	1094	425	1065	564	541	1406	107	186	546	120	715	205	143	1277	1433	992	172
Self-harmed																		
Yes	98	141	47	118	43	30	113	11	20	48	20	60	20	14	102	83	116	39
No	1422	949	375	944	520	513	1290	95	165	498	100	653	185	129	1175	1346	875	132
Total	1520	1090	422	1062	563	543	1403	106	185	546	120	713	205	143	1277	1429	991	171

	Sex		Age				Family structure (of those living with parents)					Religion				Health Status		
	Male	Female	16	17	18	19+	M&F	P&P	Step	Single	Other	CoE	Oth Chr	RC	None	Good	Fairly good	Not good
Seriously contemplated suicide																		
Yes	106	106	38	90	45	36	92	7	11	45	28	39	18	13	102	64	107	41
No	1404	974	381	962	514	504	1307	97	168	496	91	672	185	131	1160	1354	876	129
Total	1510	1080	419	1052	559	540	1399	104	179	541	119	711	203	144	1262	1418	983	170
Been bullied																		
Yes	161	159	68	142	66	44	145	14	34	64	30	83	33	20	143	139	136	44
No	1362	935	355	925	498	497	1263	93	152	476	92	631	172	125	1135	1292	857	127
Total	1523	1094	423	1067	564	541	1408	107	186	540	122	714	205	145	1278	1431	993	171
Been arrested																		
Yes	333	51	76	150	88	64	179	16	36	90	29	77	17	15	217	180	150	50
No	1176	1037	341	911	472	475	1218	90	148	450	92	635	186	126	1052	1242	835	121
Total	1509	1088	417	1061	560	539	1397	106	184	540	121	712	203	141	1269	1422	985	171
Victim of violent crime																		
Yes	268	141	70	145	109	82	196	18	35	86	27	117	20	22	197	201	159	49
No	1238	951	349	918	450	455	1203	88	149	455	91	595	182	120	1073	1223	827	121
Total	1506	1092	419	1063	559	537	1399	106	184	541	118	712	202	142	1270	1424	986	170
Victim of domestic violence																		
Yes	92	67	31	55	47	25	61	7	15	37	16	34	5	13	79	60	69	31
No	1417	1020	386	1009	511	511	1339	97	169	503	103	678	197	129	1191	1363	917	138
Total	1509	1087	417	1064	558	536	1400	104	184	540	119	712	202	142	1270	1423	986	169
Witnessed domestic violence																		
Yes	249	137	56	166	96	61	155	16	40	104	33	93	26	25	190	153	181	52
No	1258	949	360	896	462	475	1246	88	144	432	86	619	176	117	1077	1269	803	117
Total	1507	1086	416	1062	558	536	1401	104	184	536	119	712	202	142	1267	1422	984	169
Had sexual intercourse																		
Yes	1078	768	242	721	430	435	920	81	151	388	91	492	115	103	951	943	749	139
No	409	264	160	312	115	84	437	22	31	131	27	20	82	34	284	435	205	28
Total	1487	1032	402	1033	545	519	1357	103	182	519	118	693	197	137	1235	1378	954	167

	Sex		Age				Family structure (of those living with parents)					Religion				Health Status		
	Male	Female	16	17	18	19+	M&F	P&P	Step	Single	Other	CoE	Oth Chr	RC	None	Good	Fairly good	Not good
Contraception: first time																		
Yes	826	649	192	584	349	339	752	70	121	312	60	415	90	82	760	766	598	97
No	236	91	37	122	71	92	135	10	29	68	32	69	21	15	167	153	135	39
Total	1062	740	229	706	420	431	887	80	150	380	92	484	111	97	927	919	733	136
First time: wished waited																		
Yes	198	272	60	191	109	106	221	25	35	85	31	135	33	35	218	211	218	38
No	855	462	165	504	311	324	655	56	116	289	63	346	76	61	702	695	512	98
Total	1053	734	225	695	420	430	876	81	151	374	94	481	109	96	920	906	730	136
Ever had an STI																		
Yes	67	22	8	19	31	26	32	5	7	21	4	20	2	6	39	34	38	17
No	1025	733	232	712	395	407	888	75	149	367	91	483	114	94	906	914	713	119
Total	1092	755	240	731	426	433	920	80	156	388	95	503	116	100	945	948	751	136

The West Sussex lifestyle survey of young adults 16-24 year olds

This survey is about your lifestyle and how it might affect your health, well-being and lifestyle choices. The information collected will be used to help develop local services and resources that will help young people to lead healthier lifestyles. **The answers you give will be confidential and will not be seen by anyone outside the research team, so your parents and tutors will not know how you have answered.** Completing the questionnaire is voluntary. If you do not wish to answer any particular question, just leave it blank. Please read every question carefully, and answer honestly.

PERSONAL DETAILS

1. How old are you? Years ☐ ☐

2. What is your sex? Male ☐ OR Female ☐

3. What is your postcode? ☐ ☐ ☐ ☐ ☐ ☐ ☐

4. **What is your height without your shoes on in either feet and inches or centimetres?**
☐ feet ☐ ☐ inches OR ☐ ☐ ☐ centimetres

5. **Your weight in stones and pounds or kilograms?**
☐ ☐ stones ☐ ☐ pounds OR ☐ ☐ ☐ kilogram

6. **What is your ethnic group?**

White British	☐	Other Asian or	☐
White Irish	☐	Asian British	
White Other	☐	Black or Black British	☐
Mixed	☐	Chinese	☐
Indian	☐	Other ethnic group	☐
Pakistani	☐		

7. **What is your religion?**

Church of England	☐	Buddhism	☐
Other Christian	☐	Judaism	☐
Roman Catholic	☐	Sikhism	☐
Islam	☐	Other	☐
Hinduism	☐	None	☐

West Sussex **NHS**
Public Health Observatory 1

8. Apart from such special occasions as weddings, funerals and baptisms, how often do you attend services or meetings connected with your religion?

A few times a year or less ☐

At least once a month ☐

Once a week or more ☐

9. What is your marital status?

Single ☐   Married ☐   Separated (but still married) ☐

Divorced ☐   Civil partnership ☐   Widowed ☐

10. Do you live?

With parents ☐   With partner/spouse ☐   On your own ☐   With friends ☐

In shared university/ college accommodation ☐   Other ☐

11. If you live with your parent(s) or guardian(s), who do you mainly live with?

Mother and father ☐   One parent (either mother/father) ☐

Mother/father and partner ☐   In a care home ☐

Mother/father and stepparent ☐   In foster care ☐

Relatives/guardian ☐   Other ☐

12. Do you have any children?

Yes ☐   No ☐

13. Over the last 12 months, would you say your health has been:

Good ☐   Fairly good ☐   Not good ☐

SMOKING

14. Which sentence best describes you?

I have never smoked ☐   I used to smoke and have now given up ☐

I smoke occasionally ☐   I smoke regularly ☐

15. If you do smoke, about how many cigarettes a day do you smoke? (write in number)

☐☐ cigarettes

☐ I smoke less than 1 a day (tick box)

ALCOHOL

16. Which statement best describes your experience with alcohol?

I never/ hardly ever drink alcohol ☐

I occasionally drink alcohol ☐

I regularly drink alcohol ☐

2

17. If you drink, how often do you drink with the intention of getting drunk?

Never/ hardly ever ☐   Occasionally ☐   Regularly ☐

DRUGS

18. Have you ever used Cannabis?

Yes ☐   No ☐   **Please go to Question 20**

19. If you have tried Cannabis, which statement describes your current experience with Cannabis?

I used to take Cannabis, but have now stopped ☐

I occasionally take Cannabis ☐

I regularly take Cannabis ☐

20. During your lifetime have you ever used any of the following drugs?

	Never used	Occasionally use	Regularly use
Amphetamines (speed)	☐	☐	☐
Ecstasy (pills, Es)	☐	☐	☐
LSD (acid)	☐	☐	☐
Cocaine (coke)	☐	☐	☐
Ketamine (K)	☐	☐	☐
Magic Mushrooms	☐	☐	☐
Heroin (smack)	☐	☐	☐
Crack	☐	☐	☐

DIET AND EXERCISE

21. Are you . .

Vegetarian?   Yes ☐   No ☐

Vegan?   Yes ☐   No ☐

22. On an average day, how many portions of fruit and vegetables do you eat? (One portion = a serving the size of your fist)

0 ☐   1 ☐   2 ☐   3 ☐   4 ☐   5 ☐   6+ ☐

23. How often do you eat or drink the following?

	More than once a day	Once a day	Less than once a day
Sweets or chocolate	☐	☐	☐
Fast foods (crisps, chips, hamburgers)	☐	☐	☐
Fizzy Drinks e.g. coke	☐	☐	☐

3

24. How physically fit do you think you are?

Very fit ☐   fit ☐   unfit ☐   very unfit ☐

25. How do you usually travel to college/university?

Train ☐	Driving a car or van ☐	On foot ☐
Bus, minibus or coach ☐	Passenger on a car or van ☐	Other ☐
Motor cycle, scooter or moped ☐	Bicycle ☐	

26. At the present time, do you consider yourself to be:

Underweight ☐	Normal ☐	Slightly overweight ☐
Moderately overweight ☐	Very overweight ☐	

LEISURE TIME

27. On an average day, how many hours do you spend watching TV?

☐ hours   ☐☐ minutes

28. On an average day, how much time do you spend playing computer games?

☐ hours   ☐☐ minutes

29. On an average day, how much time do you spend on the Internet?

☐ hours   ☐☐ minutes

30. How frequently do you access the following on the Internet?

	Never	Occasionally	Regularly
Games	☐	☐	☐
Chat rooms/ msn	☐	☐	☐
Gambling	☐	☐	☐
Pornography	☐	☐	☐
Online shopping	☐	☐	☐
Educational	☐	☐	☐

31. Which of the newspapers mentioned below do you read regularly? Tick one

Daily Express ☐	Daily Mail ☐	Daily Mirror ☐	The Times ☐
Daily Telegraph ☐	The Independent ☐	The Daily Star ☐	Other ☐
The Sun ☐	None ☐	Guardian ☐	

32. How often do you watch "adult only" sexually explicit films or videos?

Never ☐   Occasionally ☐   Regularly ☐

4

33. How often do you watch films, videos, or play games that include explicit violence?

Never ☐ Occasionally ☐ Regularly ☐

34. In the past 12 months, have you regularly participated in organised sporting activities (e.g. football, rugby, hockey, swimming, netball, exercise classes)?

Yes ☐ No ☐

35. In the past 12 months, have you regularly participated in cultural activities (dance, music, drama) outside of college?

Yes ☐ No ☐

36. In the past 12 months, have you visited an art gallery, museum, theatre or heritage site?

Yes ☐ No ☐

37. In an average week, on how many days do you take part in physical activity for 30 minutes or more so that you are out of breath?

None ☐ 1 day ☐ 2 days ☐
3 days ☐ 4 days ☐ 5 days or more ☐

38. In the past 12 months, have you done on average two or more hours of formal volunteering (unpaid work) per week?

Yes ☐ No ☐

WELL-BEING

39. How much do you worry about failing your course?

Not at all ☐ A little ☐ A lot ☐

40. Which statement best describes your mood?

I never/hardly ever feel depressed ☐
I occasionally feel depressed ☐
I regularly feel depressed ☐

41. How often do you suffer with stress e.g. so that you feel you could not cope?

I never/ hardly ever feel stressed ☐
I occasionally feel stressed ☐
I regularly feel stressed ☐

42. In the past 12 months, on average have you felt like you get enough sleep to ensure that you can concentrate your studies?

Yes ☐ No ☐

5

43. In the past 12 months, have you ever self-harmed?

Yes ☐ No ☐

44. In the past 12 months, did you ever seriously consider attempting suicide?

Yes ☐ No ☐

CRIME AND BULLYING

45. In the past 12 months, have you been bullied?

Yes ☐ No ☐ **Please go to question 48**

46. If yes, where has the bullying mainly taken place? Tick one

At college/ university/ school ☐   On the way to/ from college/ university /school ☐

On way to/from school ☐   At work ☐   Near my home ☐

Other ☐

47. How would you describe the main form of this bullying? Tick one

Physical ☐   Verbal ☐

Virtual (text or internet) ☐   Other ☐

48. Please mark to what extent you agree with the following statements

	Strongly agree	Agree	Disagree	Strongly disagree
I feel encouraged to report bullying and aggression	☐	☐	☐	☐
I would report it when one person bullies another	☐	☐	☐	☐

49. In the past 12 months, have you ever had items such as cash, bicycle, MP3 player, mobile phone or other electrical equipment stolen?

Yes ☐ No ☐

50. In the past 12 months, have you been arrested?

Never ☐   Yes, once ☐   Yes, a few times ☐   Yes, many times ☐

51. In the past 12 months, have you vandalised somebody else's property?

Never ☐   Yes,-once ☐   Yes, a few times ☐   Yes, many times ☐

52. In the past 12 months, have you written and sprayed graffiti on walls, buses, train seats, etc?

Never ☐   Yes, once ☐   Yes, a few times ☐   Yes, many times ☐

53. In the past 12 months, have you been a victim of a violent crime?

Yes ☐ No ☐

6

54. In the past 12 months, have you been a victim of domestic violence?

Yes ☐   No ☐

55. In the past 12 months, have you witnessed domestic violence?

Yes ☐   No ☐

56. In the past 12 months, have you carried a weapon to college/university?

Yes ☐   No ☐

SEXUAL BEHAVIOUR

57. Have you had sexual intercourse?

Yes ☐   No ☐ **Please go to Question 68**

58. If yes, how old were you when you first had sexual intercourse?

☐☐ years old

59. Did you or your partner use contraception that first time or not?

Yes ☐   No ☐

60. If yes, what?

Condom ☐	Withdrawal ☐	Emergency contraception ☐
Oral contraceptive pill ☐	Safe period ☐	Other contraception ☐

61. Looking back to the first time you had sexual intercourse; do you think you should have waited longer?

Yes ☐   No ☐

62. Were you under the influence of any of the below substances when you first had sex?

Alcohol ☐   Cannabis ☐   Ecstasy ☐   Other drugs ☐   None ☐

63. What is your sexual orientation?

Heterosexual (straight) ☐	Lesbian ☐	Gay ☐
Bisexual ☐	Transsexual ☐	Unsure ☐

64. Altogether in your lifetime so far, with how many partners have you had sexual intercourse?

☐☐ partners

65. Have you ever been tested for sexually transmitted infections?

Yes ☐   No ☐

66. Have you ever had a sexually transmitted infection?

Yes ☐   No ☐

7

67. Have you ever been pregnant or got someone pregnant?

Yes ☐   No ☐

YOUR OPINION

68. Did you vote in the 2005 General Election?

Yes I voted ☐

No, I was old enough but I was not on the electoral register ☐

No, I was not aware of a general election ☐

No, I did not want to vote ☐

No, I was not old enough to vote ☐

69. Please mark how you agree with the following statement

	Agree	Not sure	Disagree
1. The introduction of tuition fees discourages young people from going to University	☐	☐	☐
2. I support identity cards	☐	☐	☐
3. The UK should withdraw from the European Union	☐	☐	☐
4. Capital punishment should be restored	☐	☐	☐
5. I do not support the smoking ban in public places	☐	☐	☐
6.I supportthe government's policy on the Iraq war	☐	☐	☐
7. The government is not strict enough on immigration	☐	☐	☐
8.The threat of terrorism is the most important issue facing society	☐	☐	☐

70. Are you interested in issues concerning your local council/area?

Yes ☐   No ☐

71. Do you feel parents in your area take enough responsibility for the behaviour of their children?

Yes ☐   No ☐

72. Do you feel people in your local area live in harmony together?

Yes ☐   No ☐

73. Please mark your personal opinion on the behaviours below by writing the number that corresponds to the key

Morally wrong =1   Morally acceptable =2   Not a moral issue=3   Depends=4   Don't Know=5

Smoking cannabis	☐	Overeating	☐
Drinking alcohol excessively	☐	Telling a lie to spare someone's feeling	☐
Sex between unmarried adults	☐	Having an abortion	☐
Gambling	☐	Married people having an affair	☐

8

74. I am supportive of a multi-cultural society

Strongly agree ☐

Agree ☐

Not sure ☐

Disagree ☐

Strongly disagree ☐

EDUCATION AND FUTURE

75. How many of the following do you have?

G.C.S.Es Grade A*-C ☐

G.C.S.Es Grade D-G ☐

None of the above ☐

I have an equivalent level 2 qualification ☐

76. What type of course are you currently studying? Tick all that apply

Introductory Diploma	☐	City and Guilds	☐
First Diploma	☐	NVQ Levels 1, 2,3	☐
BTEC National Diploma	☐	NVQ Levels 4	☐
Higher National Diploma	☐	BA /BSC (Hons)	☐
ESOL	☐	ELT	☐
National Certificate	☐	GNVQ Intermediate	☐
Foundation Degree	☐	GCSE	☐
Introductory Certificate	☐	Access	☐
CACHE Certificate/Diploma	☐	AS and A2 Level	☐
Foundation Award	☐	Post graduate course	☐

77. Is your course?

Full time ☐   Part time ☐

9

78. What sector are you aiming to find employment in at the end of your studies?

Agriculture, Horticulture and Animals ☐

Construction and Related Trades ☐

Engineering and Assembly Trades ☐

Hotel, Catering and Food Preparation Trades ☐

Clerical, Secretarial or Business Administration ☐

Leisure/Travel/Sports & Fitness ☐

Arts - Design/Media/Performing/Photography ☐

Healthcare or Education ☐

Computers or IT ☐

Motor Vehicles ☐

Sales and Distribution ☐

Uniformed Services (Security & Protective, Armed Forces) ☐

Other ☐

Don't know ☐

EMPLOYMENT

79. At the moment during term time do you do paid work .. ?

Full time ☐   Part time ☐   None ☐

80. If yes, how many hours of paid work do you do a week in term time?

☐☐ hours

81. If you have worked, do you feel your paid work has interfered with your studies?

Yes ☐   No ☐

82. What is your main source of money? Tick one

Family ☐   Job ☐   Bank loans/overdraft ☐

Savings ☐   Social Security Benefits ☐   Other ☐

83. How much debt do you predict you will have at the end of your course?

None ☐   Less than £5K ☐   £5 - 9K ☐   £9K or above ☐

84. How often do you worry about money?

Never/ hardly ever ☐   Sometimes ☐   Often ☐

10

ROAD SAFETY

85. Do you hold a full driving licence?

Yes, a car licence ☐

Yes, a motorbike licence ☐

No ☐ **Please go to Question 91**

86. To what extent do you agree with the following statements? Please circle number

	Strongly disagree						Strongly agree
I always wear my seatbelt/ helmet	1	2	3	4	5	6	7
I occasionally take risks to impress friends in the car with me	1	2	3	4	5	6	7
It is OK to speed if traffic conditions allow you to do so	1	2	3	4	5	6	7

87. Have you had any points on your license for motoring offences?

Yes ☐ No ☐

88. In the past 12 months, how often have you driven while using a hand held mobile phone?

Regularly ☐ Occasionally ☐ Never ☐

89. How frequently do you perform the following actions? Please circle number

	Never						All the time
Deliberately drive close behind a car to encourage them to speed up	1	2	3	4	5	6	7
Drive when you realise you may be over the blood alcohol limit	1	2	3	4	5	6	7
Overtake in a situation which you realise is risky	1	2	3	4	5	6	7
Drive when you've taken illicit drugs	1	2	3	4	5	6	7

90. In the past 12 months how often have you driven under the influence of . . .?

	Never	Once	More than once
Alcohol	☐	☐	☐
Illegal drugs	☐	☐	☐

91. In the past 12 months how often have you been a passenger in a car where the driver is under the influence of alcohol or illegal drugs?

Never ☐ Once ☐ More than once ☐

11

Any comments

Thank you for completing the questionnaire

West Sussex **NHS**
Public Health Observatory

12